TALES FOR A LAZY AFTERNOON

BY

SKAGIT VALLEY WRITERS LEAGUE

AUTHORS

Tales For A Lazy Afternoon

Published by Skagit Valley Writers League
www.skagitwriters.org

Layout & Design by Armchair ePublishing.
www.armchair-epublishing.weebly.com

Book Layout & Design, eBook conversions by Armchair ePublishing

Cover Art by Linda Stewart Henley

ISBN: 978-0-9821706-1-8

TALES FOR A LAZY AFTERNOON

Editing Team

Vincent E. Henley – Distributing Editor
Heidi Thomas
Judith Kirscht
Judith Landy
Kathleen Kaska
Linda Henley
Robert H. Mottram
Sharon Anderson

Cover Art

Linda Stewart Henley

Cover Design

Tony Locke - Armchair ePublishing

Dedication

To those who have gone before,
to our inspirations,
and our readers.
Thank you.

Acknowledgement

Not one book we know of has ever materialized out of thin air, and this one is no different. Our editorial board lead by the cool-headed Vincent Henley, included esteemed professional writers Heidi Thomas, Robert Mottram, Judie Landy, Kathleen Kaska, Judy Kirscht, our president, Sharon Anderson, and Linda Henley, without whose dedication to the editing process, this anthology would not be what it is today. We owe a debt of gratitude the authors who submitted their work to this endeavor and worked long and hard to polish their work, thank you. To Karla and Tony Locke, of Armchair Epublishing, we are indebted for the formatting and design of this book, for making certain we actually have a book in hand, thank you! The cover design is an original water color by artist, Linda Henley.

Table of Contents

Poetry by Guy Allen

By

Guy Allen

Winter in the Park

Winter,
snaking its first icy breath through skeletal fingers.
Branches,
stretching hopelessly through the snow crystal haze,
to a shrouded sun.
These gnarled remnants of summer green, frosted
to hide naked forms,
grudgingly greet my crunching invasion.
Creamy mallows, plodded flat.
Puddles under the crust – lurking – waiting
to pounce on a leaking boot and
flood out the warmth.
Someone has sampled this fresh early world and left
a thread of steps to mock my early rising.
Only he can own the vision of unmarked white
that enticed me from the womb of slumber
too late.

Octogenarian

A word not thought about before, has now become one to be reckoned with, as I have become one.

Webster defines octogenarian as a person whose age is in the eighties. That's pretty straight-forward, not much room for misinterpretation.

So, seventy years, the famous "three score and ten," is said to be the measure of one's life.

I hope not, that ship sailed a long time ago.

However, the Bible is adamant in Psalms 90:10:
"The days of our years are threescore years and ten, and if by reason of strength they be fourscore years, yet is their strength labour and sorrow, for it is soon cut off, and we fly away."

I'm not too sure about that last part, but it does not sound good. I'm not a fan of labor and sorrow, and I really don't like flying.

But, then again, maybe that only applied way back in the dim past when the book was put together.

Most of the folks in the Middle Ages sure didn't receive their threescore and ten allotment. Now, science sets the average lifespan in North America to be greater than threescore and seventeen, or seventy-seven.

I think I'll go with the science folk, but since I am now four score, I would appreciate it if they would kick that number up a bit.

So, what does it mean to be an octogenarian?

One thing it means is that you now have time to do all those things that you wanted to do in the middle years, when stuff like jobs and family got in the way. Too bad the physical and mental capabilities seem to be somewhat suspect. And anyway, all those things don't seem so important now.

It means that everyone, except those in your generation, seem to be getting younger, while you and your cronies age rapidly.

It means that what you want to do is more important than what you should do.

It is a time of discovery:
discovering aching muscles and bones you didn't know existed;
discovering those brown spots on your body are not freckles;
discovering that remembering friends is more important than remembering enemies;
discovering you don't have to wear a mask on Hallowe'en to scare little children;
discovering that lust and love are not mutually exclusive;
discovering that all those jokes about old people are not so funny now;
discovering that no one is interested in history, especially when it concerns what things were like when you were young;
discovering that you visit your doctor more often than you see your kids;
discovering that diapers are not just for babies;
discovering that no one cares if you lose that 20 pounds;
discovering that pensions only really work for politicians;

Just like the other stages of life, there are do's and don'ts for the octogenarian.
Don't look in a mirror unless your eyesight has failed to the point that you can't see the wrinkles.
Don't try to hide your grey hair, just shave your head or wear a hat.
Don't whistle at young women. You look ridiculous, and your dentures may pop out.
Don't pose for nude calendars.
Don't plant a walnut tree and expect to harvest the nuts.
Do spend in such a manner as to run out of life before you run out of money.

Don't waste your time giving young people advice. They don't want to hear it, and they deserve the opportunity to screw up just like you did.
Don't attempt to pay off your mortgage, you'll want to leave something for your heirs.
Do keep two diaries, one about what you wished had happened, and one of what really happened. That will confuse your descendents.
Don't let duty, obligations, or responsibilities stand in the way of enjoying what's left.
And, at the end of the day, do sit and enjoy more sunsets, yours is on the horizon.

Silhouette

Another day eases into evening

softly, with a promise of a night of love

I hear your voice and dream of the sight

of your silhouette in the light of the moon

It filters through my eyes to my soul,

searching – for that corner of memory

where your kiss belies my sadness

by the sweetness of its touch

Then I awake to the empty room

You have gone, or so it seems

you were just a silhouette

in the memory of my dreams

Guy Allen

My name is Guy Allen. I have operated most of my life as a freelance explorationist in the mineral, and oil and gas industries of North America, as well as bouts of teaching at the high school and junior college levels. My formal education consists of an Honours BSc from the University of Western Ontario. I am qualified as a Professional Engineer in British Columbia and hold high school teaching certificates for British Columbia, Alberta and Washington state.

I have both Canadian and U.S. citizenship and with my wife, Geri, I spend time equally in these two countries.

THE SWEET LIFE OF ZOMBIE DUANE

(FIRST CHAPTER EXCERPT)

BY

SHARON ANDERSON

An ancient maple stood sentinel in the front yard, its leaves, as big as dinner plates, rustled and sighed in concert with the wind. Some, already streaked amber and red, lost their hold and rode the late-October gust in graceful movement to the ground. Others, already shriveled and turning in on themselves, like severed arthritic hands pointing brittle accusing fingers, ghosted up the front porch steps and on into the open house, sliding across the wooden floors to be captured in the andirons resting neatly in the white brick fireplace. A skull embedded with precious stones and metal rested on the mantel over the white brick fireplace and as far as skulls went, seemed to convey a certain personality to the space. Waiting and watching, always waiting and watching. From the base of a modest staircase, a grandfather clock tick-tocked the hours down to minutes.

Outside the wind picked up and delivered more wrinkled-fingered leaves into the living room and shuffled opened letters and a picture across a coffee table in front of a thick cushioned couch. The mail was of no consequence, but the picture told a different story: a stick-figure drawing of a family holding hands in front of a house with the words *"Thank you"* in child's scrawl across the top and at the bottom, signed in the same writing, *"Katie"*.

Up the stairs, full-length curtains yawned into the room and floated back into place revealing a couple on a large bed. In a tangle of sheets and limbs, Brady Black moved one last time into Samantha Collins. He kissed her solidly and his lips curved into a smile.

"What?" Samantha wanted to know.

On the bedside table beyond the television remote, Brady grasped a small ornate box. He scooted up on the bed and hesitated. Then, with a bit of a flourish, he tipped back the lid to reveal a simple but elegant wedding ring. He lifted it from the box and held it up to Samantha.

"Wanna try it on?"

She sat upright and pushed her long hair out of her face. "Are you asking me something?"

Brady swallowed hard and pressed on. "Marry me. . . . Please?"

Samantha let out a long sigh. "Brady. You gotta stop with all the asking."

"I love you, Sam. Don't hold it against me."

"Maybe if you quit your job . . ." She pulled the sheet around her torso.

"Sam . . ."

The clock at the foot of the stairs chimed five times.

"You seriously thought I'd say yes this time because of a ring?"

Brady shrugged and gave her a wry smile. "It was my grandmother's . . . supposed to be good luck." He palmed it.

Samantha moved in, her hand gently resting on Brady's. "I can't put it on." She straddled him, prying the ring from his grip. The band glimmered in the filtered sunlight; no diamond, just a beautifully wrought piece of finery that spoke commitment.

"Bad luck to put it back in the box," Brady said.

She threw back the covers and winked at him. "I know what to do." She slid the ring onto Brady's middle toe on his right foot.

"Oh great. Grandma'd be so proud."

"Truly. Looks good on you," she laughed.

Brady clasped her hand and drew her back into his arms. He pressed his lips to the palm of her hand, her wrist; he kissed her shoulder, then her neck. At the sound of her sigh, he found her mouth.

"I'm sorry," she whispered.

"I'm not."

He kissed her again and again.

"I'm grateful . . ." He flipped her onto her back and pressed his hips into hers, ". . . you just saved me a ton of cash."

His lips found the exquisite edge of her jaw, "What with the church," then her porcelain neck, ". . . the priest."

His head dipped to her breast. "The band."

He lifted his head and said, "Catering!" and continued down her belly. "The way I see it, I just dodged a bullet."

"Stop it!" Samantha slapped his shoulder.

"No, really." Brady moved back up her body and tightened his arms around her frame. "I'm extremely grateful."

"Are you serious?"

"Stay," he whispered against her mouth.

"Can't." She kissed him.

"Want you."

She wriggle out of his embrace and planted her feet on the floor.

Brady propped himself up against the headboard, and watched her search for clothes. "You on tonight?"

She nodded, snatching up her panties from the floor.

"You can shower here . . . with me."

She shimmied her underwear into place and scanned the floor for her bra. "Like that's gonna get me to work on time."

Brady ran a hand through his messy hair and fished out an amulet from the side table drawer, a black stone lashed onto a rawhide strap. It was an odd thing that carried the weight of its own atmosphere. Handed down from magi to sorcerer to charlatan, the amulet enabled its master to control and direct spirits. It also allowed Brady to see Samantha's aura. As the stone settled around his neck, a small swirling ignited within it. A sparkling light shimmered around Samantha as she reached for her top. Brady smiled and waved his fingers through the light of her aura.

Samantha straightened and stared at the thing. Her eyes grew wide with shock and her mouth fell open a bit. She blinked and said, "What are you doing with that thing?"

"I'm going to the property tonight."

"You know that shit freaks me." Samantha tugged her shirt over her head. "I can't believe you put yourself in danger for total strangers."

Brady rubbed the stone and shrugged. "We've been through this."

Samantha turned and snatched up her jeans. When she turned back to Brady, her eyes were rimmed red from unshed tears. In a quieter voice, she said, "So, you think it's really haunted?"

"Last ten families lived there said so." He shrugged. "We'll see."

"But you're worried."

The light from the amulet subsided and Brady's hand fell to his side. "Nah."

"You're worried enough to wear that." She grabbed her purse. "I've gotta go."

"Sam—don't leave mad."

"Mad? I'm not mad. I'm scared. You don't owe these people anything." She started for the stairs.

Brady wrapped himself in a sheet and followed her downstairs to the front room. "I'm the only one who can help them, Sam. That has to mean something."

"You're putting total strangers before us!" She marched to the front door.

"Sam, please—I love you."

She spun around and glared. "That's why I'm leaving!" She slammed the door behind her.

Brady scooped up the child's drawing from the floor and studied it. "It's worth it, Sam, don't you see?"

One hour later, Brady stumbled across the backyard of the haunted property to his Hummer. "Just a spirit . . . just a spirit . . ." His hand shook and he fumbled the keys. Finally, he unlocked the door and climbed in. He closed his eyes and let out an unsteady breath. The house reeked of evil, ancient and powerful. A terrible image of Samantha, trussed up and broken, flashed across his mind. He knew it to be a trick of the demon, but he had to make certain she was safe.

He started the Hummer and turned the radio on.

"Welcome to our show—Whatever, Live!" The announcer began. *"Tonight we're in the studio with fellow student, Samantha Collins–it still is Collins, isn't it?"*

"Yes, Joe, it is." The very sound of her voice worked as a salve on Brady's nerves.

"That should bring smiles to the love-struck stalkers sending fan mail your way!" Joe laughed.

"Oh brother."

Brady put his rig into gear.

Across town, Joe, a turnip-shaped man in bright green suspenders and heavy glasses leaned into the radio mike. "I want to welcome a very special guest to our show tonight folks, a real treat, if I can just get him on the line . . ."

"Who is it?" Samantha adjusted her headset.

"An old friend. Okay, here we go." Joe pushed a button and the panel lit up. A dial tone rang three times before the person on the other end picked up. "A very, very old friend."

A cool, sophisticated voice answered, *"Ouch."*

"Just kidding. But you are older than dirt, right?"

"I know where you live, Joe."

He laughed. "How's the family, man?"

"Terrific."

"Girls okay?"

"Couldn't be better."

"Glad to have you onboard. We're talking about something very serious tonight, folks. So serious I had to call in a few favors to get our mystery guest on the horn."

Samantha asked, "This guy have a name?"

Joe nodded. "We're talking about how to come back from the dead. Neat little trick if you should find yourself in need."

Samantha shook her head. "How can anyone do that, Joe?"

Brady hit his blinker and turned onto River Road. "Yeah, Joe, come on."

"Well, tell us, Mr. . . . uh, Mr. Mystery," Joe began his interview.

"Cute. All right, since you're paying me so well."

"We aren't paying you at all."

"Great . . . more good news. Anyhoo, let's say you're driving on the River Road at night and you miss the hair-pin turn."

Joe agreed, "That's not good."

Brady missed the hairpin turn.

The Hummer careened onto the beach.

"There's a bonfire in your path," the mystery guest went on.

Joe laughed. *"You're screwed."*

A bonfire burned in the Hummer's path, 20 feet ahead . . . 15 . . . 10. . . . Brady slammed on the brakes. The Hummer slid sideways, pelting party-goers with sand, and rocked to a stop on a cut bank above the river. Brady gulped, let out a shaky breath, and pried his hands from the steering wheel.

"So, what, you jump out of your rig to see how many graves you'll be digging?"

"Joe, I hope you know just how wrong that truly is," Samantha said.

"You're absolutely right, Samantha," The mystery guest agreed. *"They're just children from the St. Marcus Academy out for a night of marshmallowy*

fun with their leader."

Joe growled, "Mmm, marshmallowy fun . . ."

Brady got out of his rig and faced the empty beach. Nothing but full moon and the black river rushing by. Where a bonfire had been moments ago, there was nothing but unmarred sand. The moon, full as a woman's belly in her fortieth week, lit up the sand like a million pieces of silver flashing in the mid-day sun. Brady stood akimbo next to the Hummer. "What the hell?"

"And the sand gives way . . . and you and your fine-ass Hummer fall into the river."

"Oh, no!" Samantha said. "No one ever makes it out of that river alive!"

"That's what the man's saying, Sam."

Brady leaned in the rig to turn the radio off. The sand shifted underneath him and he lost his footing. He clung to the wheel and kicked his feet out to find purchase.

"Hey, man, you okay?" A man in a black robe stood at the tail-gate. He looked like a priest, but his hair was way too long and Brady thought the dude looked high.

A group of teenagers huddled behind the man. Some holding sticks with flaming marshmallows on the ends, others with mouths ajar. The girls wore skirts and sweaters, the boys, slacks and button-downs.

"I'm sorry. I, ah, I'm not myself." Brady steadied himself against the Hummer. His vision warped and blurred, and suddenly the group of Catholic school kids wore ancient Aztec clothing, complete with loincloths and feathers. Brady looked away from the half-naked girls.

"I didn't mean to . . . I don't know what happened. Is this some kinda Halloween party?"

"Can we call someone for you?" the man said. He now wore a cape and a crazy headdress of feathers and bones.

Brady stepped back.

"Father Duane," a plump woman in a drab tunic approached the priest, "marshmallows are ready!"

"I'll be right there, Frieda." Father Duane turned to Brady. "Why don't you come, toast some marshmallows . . . call a friend."

Brady leaned into the rig to grab his keys.

The sand gave way completely.

The Hummer began a slow-motion roll. Brady wind-milled his arms backwards fighting to get away from the rig, but the vehicle was coming to him fast. The sand collapsed sending him backwards into the river. The Hummer groaned and settled on top of him, trapping him under the glacial water. The pendant bit into his chest. He couldn't move. His skin was so cold, it burned. Then he couldn't feel it.

Then he couldn't feel anything at all.

Bubbles and blood mixed together and rose to the surface of the river, as Brady Black died with his eyes wide open. From deep within his chest, a stopwatch began ticking . . .

30:00:00, 29:59:59, 29:59:58 . . .

From the beach, Father Duane crossed himself and said a quick Our Father. He then turned to his assistant. "Frieda, you'd better call 9-1-1 then get these kids home."

Frieda nodded, unable to take her eyes off the grisly site.

"I'll stick around until they fish him out," Father Duane was saying.

"Okay, Father." Frieda popped a toasted marshmallow into her mouth. "Heck of a way to end the night." She turned and herded the teens up to the road and into the church's van.

Father Duane sank to the sand and waited until a pair of EMTs showed up. The team used ropes and long poles to pull the body out of the water. They laid him on the sand and began working to revive him, even though he had been in the water over an hour. Nothing they did made any difference to the dead man. When the two men finally sat back on their haunches, Father Duane spoke up.

"Can I pray for him?" he asked.

The two EMTs exchanged a look, then shrugged.

"Yeah, go ahead," said the first.

"Nothing more we can do," said the second as they both began packing their gear and moving it to their ambulance up on the road.

Father Duane leaned over the body of Brady Black. "God have mercy," he sobbed. The priest crossed himself and placed a trembling hand on Brady's forehead.

Brady's eyes popped opened. He felt strange—not cold anymore—just strange. He looked at the man hovering over him. The man was grinning like he had never known a sad day in his entire life. Brady blinked. Some people.

"It's a miracle!" Father Duane shouted. "Oh, thank you, Father!" The priest gathered Brady into his arms and hugged him tight. "God bless yo—awk!"

Brady hugged the man back. He hugged him until there was nothing left to hug. The guy just disappeared. A jolt rushed through his body like a runaway train racing down a curvy mountain track. Wave after wave of energy funneled into his frame, flipping him onto his hands and knees.

The radio crackled from the half-submerged Hummer. "*. . . that's what you call a zombie,"* the special guest laughed.

"That's nuts," Joe said.

Samantha chimed in, *"Totally wacked."*

Back at the university radio station, Samantha sat across from Joe in Studio B and shook her head in disgust. She leaned back and crossed her arms.

Joe scratched his balding head and spoke into the mike, "So, what you're saying is you need Aztec gold."

The smug voice of the special guest sounded over the airwaves, *"That's right."*

Samantha leaned in. "And a Hoodoo man."

"Uh huh."

"Don't forget the time frame. Very important time frame." Joe made a note on a piece of paper.

Samantha sighed. "Okay, and about thirty hours."

The special guest guffawed. *"Only if you wish to reverse the Zombie Curse."*

"I feel the man, Sam," Joe said. "Some zombies may like being the way they are. Nothing wrong with that."

"Oh brother."

Brady Black sat on the beach and gazed out at the deadly black water. He didn't feel right. Something wild and dark was at work inside of him and for some strange reason, he felt for the first time in his life that his name just didn't fit him.

"Hey I don't want to get nasty letters accusing me of being insensitive to the dead." Joe laughed at his own joke.

"Nasty letters would be the least of your worries," the special guest said.

"Seriously," Disgust ripened in Samantha's voice.

"That's all the time we have tonight, folks. Thank you to our guest, Mr.—"

"My pleasure. Don't call again."

"Ha! You're killing me."

"Could happen."

"I love it. Get your kicks away from River Road tonight, folks! No sense in tempting fate on All Hallo's Eve," Joe said.

The music track to the show started up signaling the end of the broadcast. The radio fizzled off.

The two EMTs approached the body on the sand. Father Duane was nowhere in sight.

"Hey, are you okay?" the one asked.

Brady rose to his feet with the grace of a marionette whose master had just taken up the strings. He turned his head one-hundred-eighty degrees on his shoulders and fixed the two men with a cold, backwards look.

The emergency team jumped back.

"Holy shit!" cried his partner. The two men clutched each other, their eyes bugging out of their heads.

"Hey there," said Brady Black. He was feeling more and more like someone else with each passing moment. He turned his body so it was facing the same direction as his face.

"Who are you?" the first EMT dared to ask.

Brady wondered about that, too. And then it came to him. "I'm . . . Zombie Duane."

The night sky filled with garbled protests and then a sickening cryptic silence.

SHARON ANDERSON

I grew up in a haunted house in the sleepy wilds of Ballard in Washington, where front lawns seemed grander, roads wider, my dad's hands larger, and everyone was a friend or at least a potential audience member. And while our ghost never showed itself, it did make its presence known from time to time with doors mysteriously opening, lights blinking on and off, and the feeling I was never alone. A less creative person might chalk it up to older house issues and an off-the-charts imagination… I spent my time daydreaming, making up stories to share with the neighborhood kids.

A Fruitful Inquiry

By

Patricia A. Bloom

The fruit in the bowl attracted the detective. He had, as usual, missed lunch that day. A light scent from flowers, interspersed among these beckoning orbs, drifted across to him. Perhaps a little artistic touch from the lady of the house who now sat shivering, in a large wing chair correctly aligned, purposely positioned, in a corner of the room. The detective studied her ramrod straight posture, her lovely legs modestly crossed at the ankles. Only her eyes betrayed her as they darted around, looking everywhere but at him.

He looked back at the fruit, eyeing the colors—the boldness of the oranges, the brightness reflecting off the lemons, the iridescence of the purple plums, and the polished glimmer of the bowl's decorative silver acorns.

He could hear the woman muttering, her voice low and dim in an atmosphere where the air felt heavy. As his officers moved quietly through the room, carefully circumventing the body, she turned her head away, focused on some abstract plane outside the window. He had only a moment to decide, to pocket one of the fruits and sneak it away.

He plunged his hand into the bowl and felt the sharp prick of something as his fingers skittered across to his prize. He stopped and slowly pried apart the flowers, taking out each piece of fruit carefully until he could fully see the bloody knife resting on the bottom.

He lost his hunger pangs immediately.

Patricia Bloom

Patricia Bloom, Ph.D. is a research psychologist and former faculty member of the Department of Psychiatry at the University of Miami School of Medicine. At the university, she served as the director for their Center on Aging and Disabilities. During her tenure, she received her first service dog. While she writes primarily about service dogs at her blog, mymagicdog.com, she also studies and writes about unknown episodes from WWII, the results of war-time trauma and unusual mysteries.

Film is the Cure

By

Ann Bodle-Nash

It was nearly 25 years ago he first asked me, over a burger and fries in a local tavern on my lunch break, whether I had ever thought about having *a thing* with him. Caught off-guard, I reply too honestly, "Yeah but the Valley is way too small," and I change the topic. As if the question was never on the table. I look away, but the thought registers. I think about my husband.

Over the years I bump into him at our kids' school events, occasionally notice his hunched silhouette visible from my usual seat in the back row at art films, or see him dancing at the Edison Inn on Sunday evenings to the bluegrass band. His petite wife is usually along, with her amazing figure that never changes. OK, maybe she did have a facelift a few years back, but my ass will never be as small as hers, my hair never as darling, my face so chiseled, my clothes so chic.

But this fall, when I bump into him in a location I can't even remember, he asks whether I might like to go with him to a movie at the art film theatre in the next town over, a few miles away. "Sometime," he says in a nebulous off-handed way that makes me uncomfortable as to his motives. But I give him credit for noticing I am a regular at the same movies as he, and often also alone. At our ages we have learned how to go to films without a partner. He has found me out to be a lover of cinema like few in our neighborhood. He says, "Why don't you call me for a movie outing some Monday or Tuesday night when my wife is working. If your husband wouldn't mind."

He looks pretty good for all the years that have passed.

As winter approaches I think about calling him but can't summon the courage. How awkward it seems. What are the middle-aged rules for going to films with casual, opposite-sex friends I muse? Is he a player? I have surely had enough man-drama in my time to raise my head and sniff the wind. I smell caution.

On a Tuesday night, while I sit parked in a dark grocery-store lot watching my cell phone, waiting for a call-back from my husband to determine my plans for the evening, he calls. Not my husband, but my possible movie date.

"How about a movie tonight?" he says. "I'm going north to Bellingham and wonder if you might like to ride along."

"Oh," I say. "I think I have plans. I'm not sure. Holiday concert at the college."

"Well," he says, "no pressure, but if you decide you want to go call me back. If you're going alone to the concert wouldn't a movie be a better option?"

"OK, I'll think about it," I say. *No way.*

Then the past week floods back—daughter home from grad school with ten days of constant conflict and misunderstandings. Her abrupt departure. My mind still processing the conflicts, the building near-explosion of feelings-that-have-been-denied trying to keep everybody calm and civil. And I begin to think...I could use a night out to the movies.

Darkness has overcome me in the parking lot when my husband returns my call. The floodlights aren't enough to lift my spirits. I announce to my husband I'm going to the movies. He is quiet on the line, and then suggests we meet for a quick dinner first.

I meet him for a quick senior meal at Bob's, the local diner, then drive to my new-movie-friend's house, which I have never been to. Ever.

After some searching I find the misshapen mailbox with the numbers that match those he has recited. He lives in the countryside at the end of a long, poorly lit, graveled driveway. His porch light is on, and he steps out at the sound of my car.

My friend-the-movie-date says, "Park your car there," and points to a spot near an evergreen hedge. "I'll drive, but let's take my work van because my other car's heater doesn't work. You OK with that?" And it is a cold, cold, cold night.

The stars are brilliant in his rural backyard, and I can see clearly into Canada. I take a look at the van and think, what the hell. "Watch the step up and grab the handle," he says.

We wind up the freeway toward the North Star, the van noisy with work paraphernalia bouncing around the back—empty buckets, scraps of vinyl, carpet, craftsman's tools. He makes conversation above the road noise, but I notice he leans toward me when I speak. His right ear brushes my left shoulder, leading me to guess his hearing is shot. I lean into the narrow space between us and yell back to be understood.

Suddenly I feel I am on an adventure with a stranger, a runaway in a van my mother would never have allowed me in, or I my daughters. We are headed to a bank heist in the getaway vehicle. The grin comes on and I can't contain it. The freedom of the road tugs.

He parks the utility van in a dark lot near the theater. My hand is on the door when he says, "Hey wait a minute, I have to get my head straight before the movie." I freeze. He opens the glove box, removes a small wooden box with a sliding lid, and pops out a fat joint. "It's legal now," he says.

Everything stops for a second. I think about my kids and what they would think of their mom in a van, in a dark parking lot, with a crazy man who plans to smoke his legal joint before going into a controversial French film with nudity galore, all in the name of an obsession with French films... and I begin to laugh.

It's a laugh I have been saving for weeks. The absurdity of the moment overwhelms me, the inattention to correctness, the moment I feel twenty-two again. Before marriage, kids, house payments, college tuition, daughter's seizures in San Francisco and Chicago. Before the call from the state police and her grad school professor. The twisted stomach I get with each call. The fear I so often feel for her. The powerlessness. The love I have for a daughter I can't keep safe no matter how hard I try, for she is a grown woman facing down her demons.

I say to this man, "You go ahead. My drug is just being out for the evening in a vehicle that would work in a bank robbery." I have no idea why I say this to him. I do not want to rob a bank.

He looks puzzled for an instant, confused as if I am a crazy woman he just picked up instead of a long time casual acquaintance. He has no idea what I'm talking about, but I know, and I take my fantasy into the film and enjoy every scene. The French language comforts me, washes over me, forcing concentration on something outside myself, comprehension dragging its heels from a cobwebbed corner of my brain. I compare the subtitles to the spoken word, think how I've never been inside a French lycée, never to a lesbian bar in Lille, and that I will never really understand French culture. I think about all the good in my life. I breathe.

Afterward we ride south toward home dissecting the film. The van's heater pours it out. Our perceptions of the film differ vastly, and it matters not to me. The night is clear, the stars brilliant, frost forming in the ditches.

Ann Bodle-Nash

Ann Bodle-Nash has lived in the Skagit Valley since 1977. She writes fiction and non-fiction with special regard to the nuances within interpersonal relationships. She also loves to fish.

Discovering America

By

Ann Brittain

In nineteen-eighteen, my grandparents immigrated to America from Norway. They settled in New York City. It didn't take long for Grandpa Fritz, a skilled tailor, to find work in the garment district. He learned to love the big city and the opportunities it presented, but he sorely missed spending time with his family. Returning late in the evening, numb from exhaustion, he'd eat a lukewarm meal before he fell into bed. Fritz rarely saw his sons, Per and Eric, but he understood that creating a better life for his children was his first priority.

Unlike her husband, Grandma Asta hated New York, hated their tiny apartment, and hated the other tenants who lived in their building. The disgusting smell of foreign spices and sweat permeated the air around her. She longed to find a woman friend, someone to console and support her, but none of her neighbors spoke Norwegian. They tried to communicate with gestures and pointing, but it was an unsatisfying exchange.

Asta began to resent Fritz for disrupting their quiet lives in the old country. As the days passed, she prayed that he would realize his dream had become a terrible mistake and let them go back to Norway.

One morning, three months after they arrived, nausea overwhelmed Asta. To her horror, she realized she was pregnant. The thought of giving birth to a child in this awful place filled her with fear. Seven months later, she delivered another healthy son.

Fritz beamed when he came home to find his wife holding their infant. "Asta," he cupped her cheek. "Three sons, what a wonderful start to our family."

Start? Asta thought as a wave of horror washed through her. He must be crazy. She would not have another child in this foreign land. Avoiding the expectant gleam in his eyes, she turned her face to the wall.

"What shall we name him?" Fritz massaged his jaw. "I know. Bjarne, a strong Norwegian name."

"Bjarne, well I..." Weariness tugged at Asta's eyelids. She had wanted to name the baby Victor after her father, but what did it matter? "Yes, that is a fine name."

To Asta's dismay, Bjarne started to walk at nine months. Soon the baby began pulling himself up on the furniture navigating a path around the apartment supported by chairs and tables. By the time he was ten months old, he was fully mobile and determined to trail after his older brothers as they bolted out the door.

One evening Asta stood over the stove daydreaming about the little pond near her home in Larvik. She stirred the kettle of fish soup and paused. When had the room become so quiet? Whirling around, her eyes flew to the corner where she'd left Bjarne drumming on a copper bowl. He wasn't there or anywhere else within her sight. Asta spotted the door ajar.

She slapped the wooden spoon down on the counter. Would Per and Eric ever learn to shut it properly? Now the baby had wandered after them. She rushed to the window. Down on the street, her older sons were playing stickball with the neighborhood children, but Bjarne was not there. Bolting to the top of the stairs Asta spotted her copper bowl upside down on floor below.

She sprinted down the stairs to the second floor. Casting a quick glance into long hallway, relief swelled her chest. Bjarne, wobbling on his chubby legs, stood in the middle of the corridor. "You bad boy," she admonished and strode toward him.

Swinging the baby into her arms, she caught sight of an open apartment door. The acrid odor of smoke wafted from within the room. Holding Bjarne firmly against her hip she stepped forward. If something was on fire inside, it could burn the building down. Peering through the opening, Asta rapped her knuckles against the door jamb.

"Hello." She waited a moment but no one appeared. Entering the apartment, Asta spied a charred loaf of what appeared to be pumpernickel bread on the counter. Her tense muscles relaxed. The smell had been the result of poor cookery not menacing flames. Satisfied that a disaster was not in the offing, she turned to leave and froze. A slick red stain trailed along the fringed edge of the worn carpet dotting a path across the room to the corner. A woman sat crumpled against the wall like an abandoned marionette. Drying blood matted her long auburn hair and her green eyes stared lifelessly at the ceiling.

A scream ripped from Asta's throat. Clutching the baby, she bolted into the hall, stumbled up the steps and dove into her apartment.

Hours later, Fritz burst in. "Oh my god, Asta. I just spoke to the police. They said a woman downstairs was murdered." He gulped, moving his mouth as if unable to speak. "It is so distressing that you found her like that. My dear, are you all right?"

Fritz knelt by her chair and tried to take her hand, but Asta jerked it from his grasp. "I am going home," she hissed through taut lips.

"What?" Fritz pulled off his cap." We can't go back now. I got a promotion today. We'll have more money. We can move—"

"You stay in this horrible country if you must, but I am taking the boys and leaving."

"We can't afford—"

"Uncle Peter will wire the money," Asta snapped. "I don't care if it takes me the rest of my life to pay him back."

Living in America without his family was something Grandpa could not do. A month later they boarded a ship bound for Norway. Fritz thought often of his days in the states. He filled his sons' heads with stories of the bustling streets of New York City and his unrealized fantasy of a wonderful new life there.

Per and Eric listened to their father's accounts of the big city as if they were fairytales, but his father's words resonated in Bjarne's ears. When the boy learned that the exciting country his father described was his birthplace, his heart burst with pride. In his dreams Bjarne envisioned that one day he would return to discover his own America.

Elaina

By

Melba Burke

From whence do I come? Whither do I go? These are the questions I ask of thee.

A thick spattering of long, ebony hair flutters in the breeze as Elaina hoists herself onto the massive trunk of a downed cottonwood tree. She examines the tree trunk, polished eons ago by the ebb and flow of the tides. She scrapes a sample of the tree's DNA onto a gooey leaf of her receptacle pouch. When the receptacle is full, it protrudes like a tree burl. Come dusk, her pouch will be filled, likely. The pouch is a distasteful part of her anatomy, a genetic mutation attached to her pelvis, a design of Nolan Angler of Stellar Tech.

Elaina pats the pouch. Thoughts of pregnancy wisp through her mind. The collection of DNA is the closest she will ever come to giving birth to a live organism. She is sterile, as are all other second generations like her.

Elaina is in no hurry to fill her pouch this morning. She becomes engrossed in the subtle changes of her surroundings—the shifting shades of dawn, the sound of water lapping, and the squawk of gulls. Her body relaxes, all five foot nine inches of her. She closes her eyes and listens, intoxicated by the music of the dawn's breaking. Her surroundings are adaptations from planet Earth in the Milky Way Galaxy. The animal and plant life, like her, were regenerated by Stellar Tech from preserved samples of Earthen and Triangula DNA.

Elaina imagines a new life stirring within her. Her hand caresses the area where her pouch is attached to her body, the place where a woman of the humanoid species would carry a child. The intensity of her maternal desire surprises her and her cheeks redden as if her private thoughts are being read by the *Ancestors* or assimilated by another of her kind.

Something stirs under her finger tips. She feels movement.

"Could it be?"

She explores further.

"No."

Confused, Elaina examines her pouch and finds nothing alive amongst its leaves.

The breeze shifts and quickens. The temperature drops. Gulls stop squawking. Goose bumps cascade down her arms. She shivers and turns down the sleeves of her blouse. She searches the sea, expecting to see a squall and is disturbed by the calmness of the water.

"Something is not right."

She trembles. Images cascade through her mind . . . images of darkness and light . . . images of distant galaxies, planets, and star systems. Images of life forms distinct from her in their adaptations but similar in origin. Images of a gaseous mass of molecules traveling the universe, shapeless but . . . .

"What's happening to me?"

Her tongue slides across her lips and her body releases a *querk*, a force equivalent to many bolts of lightning. Her hair rises upward emitting a frizzling pop. Lights flash. Ripples cascade across the sea swelling into ominous waves. Her mind unhinges and she collapses into a deep stupor.

She is awakened by the burning rays of the midday sun . . . lying prone on the sand where she must have fallen from the driftwood. Flashes of memory seep into her consciousness. She pushes them away as one might a nightmare. She rises, dusts off her salmon-colored coveralls and gawks in disbelief at the birds and fish littering the beach, lifeless. Her eyes close, sickened by the sight and smell of the devastation before her.

"Did I do this?"

She sinks to her knees examining the mountains in the distance expecting to be disciplined, and prostrates herself, terrified. The mountain tops are purple. The lower parts are dark shades of blue, and green. A misty fog is midway up the mountain. The fog beckons her. She shudders.

"The mountain mist, the *Ancestors*." Elaina's voice sounds distant, detached as she utters the words.

The directives of the *Ancestors* pulse through her like a beacon that directs the passage of transports through intergalactic space. Gravity anchors Planet VOX93 amid the multitude of stars and planets of the Triangulum Galaxy. Elaina is anchored by the constraints of her fear.

The *Ancestors* expect, no, demand, that Elaina comply with the program spliced into her genetic code. Inwardly Elaina knows she must comply. In addition she must reconcile the surge, the discharge of energy, the *querk*. Her life depends upon her doing so.

The bond that she shares with the Triangoids, the original inhabitants of Planet VOX93, draws her from her cowering position and gives her the resolve to find a solution to her dilemma. She must reach Safe Harbor. She must find the oldest of her kind. She must make peace with the *Ancestors* before Stellar Tech tracks her down and terminates her.

She gathers her hair to the top of her head and secures it with a clasp. Elaina walks hastily in the direction of Safe Harbor. Her progress is slowed by an accumulation of clutter and debris drawn to her like a magnet. Irritated by the growing piles of clutter, she discharges a surge of energy. The debris is thrust away from her spiraling skyward. No heed is given to the objects, by her, as they fall back to the planet's surface behind her. She is determined to remain steadfast in her resolve despite the obstacles she may encounter along the way. For protection from those that might pursue her, she hugs the cover of saplings growing along the edge of the forest near the sea. She expects retaliation in some form from the *Ancestors* or the seafaring vessel displaying the colors of Stellar Tech making its way toward Safe Harbor. She is surprised and relieved when no further delays are encountered.

Before the afternoon shadows lengthen, she enters the core of Safe Harbor. She is exhausted, but is not put off by her physical discomfort; she continues her search for the oldest of her kind…the vintage remains of a first generation mutant named Samantha, known simply as Sam. Sam is the last survivor of the Rogue War of 200,068, a war waged between mutants and humanoids over the right to exist on equal terms. The war nearly destroyed Planet VOX93. Extinction threatened the existence of the Triangula, who were banished from VOX93 after the war, and forced to travel the universe in molecular form as space dust. None of the first generation male or female mutant Triangoids survived except Sam. Every first generation mutant was terminated by the Inter Galactic Council. Nolan Angler of Stellar Tech harvested Triangula DNA samples before their banishment and developed a race of second generation all-female mutant Triangoids controlled by the Mountain Mist Program.

Elaina finds Sam in the tactical room gazing out a window overlooking a courtyard. Elaina has never met Sam, but would recognize her anywhere, Sam's history as the instigator of the Rogue War is well known to second generation mutants. A poster with her picture hangs on a wall in the entrance of Stellar Tech as a reminder of the futility of war.

During DNA Collection Training, a clerk working in the records department of Stellar Tech, told Elaina that although Sam is listed among the terminated she could be found in the old tactical building if Elaina ever had need of her. Elaina hadn't thought much about what was said at the time, but today she is gratified that the information is correct.

"I have done it, really done it." Objects from the room start to cluster around Elaina.

Sam turns from the window to examine the intruder, with frizzed hair and an ever growing pile of clutter moving toward her. The furniture, Sam notices, moves in cadence with the stranger's steps.

The mutant fingers the strands of her hair standing on end. A scowl knits her brows. Her shoulders slump at the menagerie closing in around her. Sam dodges a chair and bumps into the conference table, which is dust-ridden.

"The mutant is disturbed and with good reason...."

She observes Elaina, as a mother might her child, realizing this was her, fifty years ago.

The disarray of Elaina and the room rekindles memories that disturb and consume her, like the flames of a raging fire. Sam has avoided this room purposely; it reminds her of the death of her mother. Her face pales. The ashen color is intensified by the blue-black of her hair which is tied back with a yellow ribbon. The ribbon was a gift from her mother. It is her most cherished possession.

"Why did I enter this room today? Why did she have to find me here?" she asks herself.

Sam listens to the rhythmic clank of clutter compete with Elaina's sputters. She would like to laugh, despite her feeling of moroseness, but refrains from doing so. She remains silent and allows the chaos around her to continue, choosing not to interfere. Her observations feed her curiosity. She glances about and her expectations swell. She leans forward awaiting Elaina's next words.

"Something's happened to me." Elaina blurts in exasperation.

Unable to control her movements, she twirls headlong into Sam who is caught up in Elaina's burst of energy. Like the chairs, Sam mirrors her movements. They dance like marionettes. Elaina moves back. Sam moves forward. Elaina circles. Sam follows. They appraise each other in the flutter of activity. One is strong and determined. The other is unsure... fearful.

Sam's finger reaches out and Elaina's finger is drawn to it. They touch. A spark flares through Sam, and she is drawn into the events of Elaina's life. Pictures and sensations whirl through Sam's mind as she assimilates Elaina's past. Sam sorts until she reaches that morning's episode where Elaina is stretched out on driftwood. It's been awhile since Sam has known the peace and contentment evident in Elaina's expression. Sam shifts in her chair and smiles.

Elaina's heart skips a beat and she falters. The tall gangly brunette's nerves are stretched taut. When she peers into Sam's eyes, they are glazed over. Unable to make sense of Sam's facial expressions Elaina places her hands on her hips. The furniture jumps.

"Are you laughing at what happened to me?" Elaina demands.

"No," Sam insists, almost having forgotten Elaina's presence. "Settle down. I think I know what's happening to you. You are evolving, Elaina... becoming like me. I knew it would happen sometime...to someone... someday." Her voice is eager and inviting as is her expression tinged with excitement. Like she has found a long lost treasure, which in truth she has.

"Like you? How can I? I'm second generation." Elaina chooses her words carefully, reminding Sam that there are differences between them, not sure how much Sam learned about her during her assimilation.

After all, she doesn't yet know Sam...really. She wonders if Sam has seen those shapeless molecules that travel the universe, the Triangula. Space dust, as Stellar Tech calls it. The stuff, the Triangula are made of.

Sam's fingers smooth Elaina's hair and she reaches down to right Elaina's rising skirt.

"We control the flow of energy." Sam lowers her chin to look into Elaina's eyes. "Do you have any idea what that means?"

Sam knows full well that Elaina does, but it is not her place to tell Elaina what she needs to disclose. Sam must allow Elaina to reveal her secrets. After all, she is not the Mountain Mist Program. The Program is an invention of Stellar Tech. It still holds the mutants on this planet captive.

"Control the flow of energy...? No one can do that...." The space furrows between Elaina's brows.

"We can, Elaina, you and I, we've evolved beyond the control of Stellar Tech and the Mountain Mist Program."

Elaina stumbles to her feet. The furniture stays put. Disturbed by the sudden silence, Elaina glances up at Sam.

Sam raises her brows, "See?"

"What of *my* purpose?"

Elaina is not speaking of her role as a collector of DNA, but she does not say more. She craves a deeper purpose. The preservation of Planet VOX93 for a Triangula species like her, unshackled. Free of the Mountain Mist Program and Stellar Tech.

Sam places a hand on her shoulder.

"What will the *Ancestors* do to me?" Elaina shivers. "Will you help me?"

"What do you require of me?" Sam pries.

"I want to be unshackled." Elaina trembles, remembering the sense of freedom she felt as she lay on the log. "I want to make the warmth of the sun, to shift color, to channel the wind, and to control *querks*."

"You want to choose what you do?" Sam's voice drops to a whisper, "You are more than a tool guided by a nebulous mist in the mountain."

"Nebulous?" Is that what Sam thinks of the Mountain Mist Program and Stellar Tech? She settles into her chair, relaxed for the first time since entering the tactical room.

Sam senses that Elaina is ready for a change and decides not to dally any longer. "Wouldn't you want to feel the contentment you did this morning every day, Elaina?"

"Yes, well ... maybe...." Elaina responds.

Sam takes Elaina's words as a yes, and without asking Elaina's permission or giving the outcome of her actions a second thought, Sam transforms Elaina's appearance into the likeness of a hybrid humanoid. Her hair she changes to a fiery red, her eyes to a gray blue—like after a storm. Her body she gives a lusty, engaging plumpness.

"This appearance will set you apart from second generation Triangoid mutants." Sam says.

Elaina's mouth drops open. Words escape her. She gasps and gulps in disbelief. She does not recognize herself.

Before Elaina has a chance to react further, Sam proceeds to remove Elaina's receptacle pouch leaving only a remnant the size of a small pocket triggering her latent reproductive system. She also removes and turns off the *Mountain Mist Program* implant that tethers Elaina's free will, disintegrating Elaina's allegiance to the *Ancestors*. In its place emerges a new directive, a firm desire to reproduce an un-tethered race of hybrid Triangoids.

"You already possess a keen, curious intellect, and a gifted mind," says Sam, circling Elaina, assessing her reaction to her transformation. Other than her initial shock she senses nothing from Elaina that worries her.

"Your assimilation skills will remain intact and you can still collect small amounts of DNA for replication."

Sam observes, as Elaina's past experiences kaleidoscope through her establishing her new identity. Sam expects Elaina to be overwhelmed... but she is not. The strength of Elaina's will and quick adaptation to change is surprising.

"The squall with Stellar Tech and the *Ancestors* has just begun," Elaina whispers in Sam's ear.

Sam nods her agreement. "This room buzzed with activity when there were others like me before the war, before termination, and before my transformation," she informs Elaina. "Every mutant, though similar in appearance and abilities, is wired for the completion of specific tasks. Mine was to maintain the stability of the planet's core and promote its geological evolution."

Elaina helps Sam dust the tactical table, and right the chairs. "Mine was to collect DNA for replication up until moments ago. My plan now, is to replicate others like me."

Sam reappraises Elaina wistfully, noting how her behavior changed with her transformation.

"How else would I have survived all these generations, Elaina? You will learn to value these changes as I have. Stellar Tech will be hunting you as they hunt me. The records department at Stellar Tech has already reported you missing."

"Sam, let's right the wrongs of Stellar Tech."

"I'm with you, Elaina." Sam responds swiftly with commitment. Her eyes sparkle. "Let's free all our sisters."

Elaina nods her approval, and then adds, "Sam, don't you think it would be nice to have children underfoot once again?"

Sam reaches for the yellow ribbon in her hair and imagines her mother holding her. She breathes deeply and answers, "Yes it would, Elaina. Yes it would."

Melba Burke

Melba Burke is of Native American heritage. She was born in North Dakota and currently resides in the Pacific Northwest. Her interest in writing science fiction developed early in life, triggered by her maternal grandmother's sighting of a flying saucer which has become a family legend passed down to succeeding generations extending even to one of Burke's daughters who earned a Doctorate in Astronomy and became a Professor of Physics and Astronomy at Texas Christian University. She is engaged in writing a science fiction novel, Planet VOX93. Her first publication is the science fiction short story, Elaina.

A Midnight Meeting

A Forever Fey Story

By

Màiri Campbell

Ashleigh felt the walls closing in on her. She had to get away from everything and everyone... at least for a while. She pulled on black leggings, a snug black tank top and her thigh-high black leather boots, as she had countless times before. An outfit perfect for blending into the shadows. She took her cloak from the closet and walked out the door.

Ashleigh gathered her long chestnut locks forward over her shoulder, settling her cloak around herself and pulled the hood up. The fur trim tickled her face. That small reminder of days gone by only served to depress her more. She stepped off the porch and into the night.

Her mind wandered back in time to when she lived with her friends, Malcolm and Kaitlin, people she cared about, and who cared about her. She stroked the soft pelt of the badger and thought of the farmer who had gotten angry after a badger almost killed his hound. He had poisoned the female and her kits, leaving them to rot.

Malcolm had skinned and tanned the badger hides. Doing what he could to make their deaths more meaningful than just letting them decay. He had given the pelt of the female to Kaitlin to use on the cloak she was making for Ashleigh. Her friends were part of a local lycan pack. The pack was not happy about the badgers being poisoned. They did a few things to drive the farmer from the area. No one told her exactly what they had done to make him leave, no matter how many times she asked.

Thoughts of Malcolm, Kaitlin and their children brought tears to her eyes. She missed her dear friends. They were the closest thing to family she'd had since being turned. Sadly, the kids became ill one day after ingesting tainted meat and did not survive. They had been out playing, slipping the watchful eye of the mother, and found what appeared to be a recently shot deer. In truth, it was a tainted carcass that had been placed out to decrease the local wolf and coyote population. Malcolm and Kaitlin were never the same after that, and had moved away to start over. They had asked Ashleigh to go with them, but she had insisted it was time for her to head home.

And now here she was, in Chicago, where it had all started for her so long ago. She had been walking aimlessly, when she paused to get her bearings. She noticed she was just outside what is now Burnham Park. Many things had changed in the eighty-seven years she'd been gone. She remembered when single dwelling hovels covered the area—the park was a great improvement.

Casting about, she spied an alley and slipped into its shadows. It didn't take long to find one of the city's many homeless people. She fed quickly, taking just enough blood to stave off the cravings. She left the man lying as comfortably as she could; he would be a bit weak, but he would live.

Straightening her cloak, Ashleigh glanced around to make sure no one was watching before heading into the park across the street. Choosing a bench under a burnt out lamp post, she sat down, letting her mind wander through old memories.

There were many things and people that she missed from her past. Now there were others, new friends, new things, that she would miss just as much when they too were gone. So deeply lost in thought, Ashleigh did not sense, or hear, the person approaching her until she spoke.

Varruka stomped down the hill with the ferocity of one wronged, mumbling to herself incoherently. She was in the mood for the park's serene solitude tonight, so she'd taken a taxi from the library to the park—only to be ripped off by the taxi driver. She was certain his meter was rigged. She should have just run. It would have been faster, but she missed doing mundane human things. Hell, she missed being human.

But she was here now and made her way down to the lake's edge when she froze, sniffing the air. It was definitely not human, not musky enough to be any sort of were-creature; it was sweet and sour at the same time and impossibly familiar... vampire. Varruka paused long enough to focus on where the scent was coming from. A moment later she saw it, a female, sitting on a bench right by the lake. Annoyed that someone was sitting where she wanted to be, Varruka started walking again, stopping just beside the bench. She stood there glaring at the girl, taking in the perfect porcelain face. Her irritation spiked.

Shifting her weight so she stood with one hip cocked and her arms folded across her chest, she growled, "Do I know you?"

The question was meant as a conversation starter, but the girl really did look vaguely familiar to her. *Where had she seen her before? Chicago? Surely not. She would remember a face so annoyingly perfect. A picture somewhere? The newspaper?* Nothing seemed to match up, but it didn't matter. Varruka refused to let down her guard until she knew beyond all certainty that the vampire she was looking at was not a threat to her.

Ashleigh blinked as she brought herself back to the here and now. She turned her head slightly to look at the woman standing near the end of the bench. As she considered the slightly acidic question she noted the torn jeans, over-sized t-shirt under a denim jacket, the sneakers that had seen better days. Shifting her body sideways, she draped a slender arm over the back of the bench and laced her fingers together, looking directly at the woman. The stranger appeared to be around eighteen or nineteen years of age, but Ashleigh knew that was false, since the stranger was a vampire like herself.

With a slight look of annoyance, Ashleigh raised her perfectly groomed brow.

"I don't believe so. I at least would remember the sound of your voice, if that is how you always speak to others." Ashleigh sniffed and wondered what it was with the female vamps here? She had never met any as rude as the ones here in Chicago. They all seemed to be snotty little wenches that didn't know how to get along with others. While Ashleigh preferred not to make a habit of associating with other vampires, she didn't mind the occasional social interaction.

Turning back to the water, she inquired, "Have you been having a bad night or did someone have garlic in their veins?" She didn't want to deal with someone else's drama, especially someone that she didn't know. The girl was here and did not seem about to leave any time soon. She shifted her gaze back to the girl.

"Neither. Not that it's any of your business." Varruka tightened her arms around herself, raising her own eyebrow in response. She didn't know exactly how old, but she could sense the other woman was at least twice her own age from the power that pulsed around her. This meant she was also twice as strong and fast. Perhaps treating this vamp the way she normally treated others would not be her wisest move.

The black water shifted and rippled in the light breeze, lapping gently at the shore. So what if she was having a bad night? She wasn't about to spill her heart to a complete stranger. It didn't matter that the woman was a vampire, too. She had learned that lesson fast and hard. Watching the woman from the corner of her eye, Varruka wondered if she could best her in a fight if she needed to.

Ashleigh didn't believe the girl for a minute, she knew the look of someone having a shitty day, and gods knew she'd lived through enough of her own. Whatever it was, it couldn't be man trouble. The girl was very pretty and should be able to attract men without difficulty. Unless of course her tongue was always acidic, men didn't usually find that attractive.

"I'm Ashleigh by the way. And staring at me like that will get you nowhere honey. I prefer men." She couldn't quite control the smile that was playing around the corners of her mouth. She was feeling melancholy, which usually put her in a slightly crabby mood. *Where the hell is Bran when I need him? He would know the right things to say.* The thought of her best friend, as always, softened the look in her eye, put a smile on her lips, and gentled her tone.

"Sorry, it would appear I'm not in such a wonderful mood myself." Ashleigh turned to stretch out her legs, crossing them at the ankles. Tipping her head back to look up at the stars she added, "You can sit if you want, I don't mind. I won't bite."

"You're not my type sweetheart, not for biting or anything else." Varruka gave a derisive snort. "So don't flatter yourself." Taking a few steps toward the lake, Varruka snatched a smooth stone from the ground, flicking it out over the water. It skipped a good dozen times before it sank into the watery depths. After a long pause, she turned and glanced at the older woman. She'd said her name was Ashleigh. The name sounded vaguely familiar; sort of like a memory from a time long forgotten.

Ashleigh couldn't help the snicker that escaped when the girl told her not to flatter herself. "Well, the way you'd been staring at me, one would beg to differ." She watched as the younger woman took a few steps towards the lake. She did appear to be upset about something, but it wasn't Ashleigh's problem.

With a soft sigh Varruka turned and trudged over to the bench. "Varruka. My name is Varruka." She found herself suddenly and inexplicably exhausted, far too tired to try and continue on with a battle of wits. Lowering herself onto the bench, Varruka quickly drew her legs up to her chest, wrapping her arms around them protectively.

Ashleigh watched the girl from the corner of her eye as she sat down, curling up into herself.

"Varruka, what a pretty name, unusual too," she commented quietly. *Man, the girl looked like some lost little waif.* Ashleigh had the urge to hand her a chocolate bar, pat her on the head and tell her, *"It's okay little girl, Santa's real."* She had to give herself a bit of a shake to rid her mind of that little scene.

"Thanks," Varruka mumbled in response to the compliment. She knew well enough that her name was rare, but she'd had it so damn long it hardly bothered her anymore, not like it had in her youth—what little she remembered of that time. She seemed to recall being picked on by other kids her age. Decades ago, the teasing had bothered her. Now, an outcast to society and veritable lone wolf, she hardly even remembered how to function in simple social situations—like this one.

She sat with her chin on her knees, staring out over the lake, closing her eyes for a few moments before opening them again. Turning her head, Varruka laid her cheek upon her knees as her gaze settled on the older vampire.

"So, Ashleigh," she began, her tone notably friendlier than before, though still wary. "I've haven't seen you around. Are you new to Chicago?"

"No, not new, not really. I was born here, long, long ago," Ashleigh replied. "Though I have been gone and only came back a few months ago. What about yourself?"

Varruka sighed heavily, almost reluctant to have a civil conversation with the woman beside her. Still, her mouth opened of its own accord in response. "I've lived in Chicago for years." She paused briefly before she remembered that the girl beside her was a fellow vampire, and continued. "Seventy-eight years, actually. Since my birth, or rebirth, I should say. I used to hate it here, but now... I love this city." Her gaze narrowed.

"Why the long departure? Did you leave to see a beau?" Not all vampires had Varruka's dead social life... or rather, undead social life.

Ashleigh couldn't stop the shudder that raked her body as memories crowded her mind. "I was born here too, both births. My master," she spat the word, "took me and others he had created, gathered us all up, and took us back to his sanctuary just outside of town. It was many years before I escaped." She gave Varruka a small smile, "Sorry, but thoughts of that murderous bastard always depress me." Then a slow wicked smile eased its way across her features she added, "That is, until I remember how satisfying it was to kill him. So no, it wasn't to see a beau."

"You... you killed your master?" Varruka whispered, eyes wide in awe. She straightened up, at least as much as she could while she kept her arms wrapped around her legs. "The masters say if you kill them those they made die too. But you're saying you killed yours?"

"They tell us that so we won't kill them." Ashleigh turned her gaze towards the lake in front of them as that dark time from her past came flooding back. She didn't like thinking about it, and she had only ever discussed it with Malcolm and Kaitlin, and years later, Bran. It was not a time of her life that she liked to remember. She took a deep breath.

"My father was killed trying to protect me. My Master, as he demanded to be called, turned me right there with my father's blank eyes watching, and his blood soaking into my clothes. Soon after, I was taught many things about how to please a man, or—at least for pleasing *him*. I was one of many females he kept for personal amusement. After a few years he shared me with his special friends."

Varruka's lips parted in a silent *oh* as she listened. She had thought it was just her master who had done things like that. She turned on the bench, her legs dropping down, her hands fluttering about in her lap before finally clasping one in the other.

Ashleigh paused, taking a shuddering breath. Her mind shied away from the memories that were flooding back. "We were treated worse than his broodmares. He passed us around like party favors once he grew tired of keeping us to himself. Those who were disobedient were punished. He seemed to take great joy in beating us, me especially. I refused to be the quiet complacent female, for him and his friends to do whatever they wanted to do to me. I've only told three other people this. Not really certain why I'm now telling you."

"I thought, I mean, I..." Varruka stammered before clamping her lips together. After a deep breath, she tried again, "I thought only my creator did that. I never knew that other masters did that to those they turned. How did you get away? It doesn't sound like he would've just let you go."

"Oh, he wouldn't have. He took pleasure in telling me that. He used to promise me that when he finally grew tired of me, he would keep me just to torture me. He kept that promise for almost eighty years. Then I found a way to kill him and escape."

"Weren't you afraid the other masters would come after you? I know

I would have been."

Ashleigh shook her head and smirked. "Nope, I didn't worry about that at all. I left a very clear message for all of his friends before I left. I put that bastard's head on a pike outside his compound."

"No way! That… that was you? That happened to *my* master! At the time, I was not there, I was out on *loan*. You're the reason I'm free!" Varruka exclaimed. "That's why you look familiar! Our master had paintings of you all over the manor house."

"Yes, he did. I'm sorry; I don't remember you from that time."

"It's okay. I'd only been there three years before you killed him," Varruka grinned. "Everyone was surprised when the masters who had some of us on loan just dumped us out at the house. They left us there to fend for ourselves."

"Good. That means they all understood the warning I left when I put his head on that pike." The smile that graced Ashleigh's face could only be described as evil.

"No one at the house that day would tell the rest of us what happened. Or who had killed him." Varruka said.

"They were trying to help protect me. I would have been hunted down for sure if they had talked. The other two who distracted him for me; they would surely have been killed had anyone talked."

"There were rumors that the other masters were going to hunt you. But they didn't seem too interested."

"Our master was one of *the* strongest vampires around at the time I killed him. Placing his head on that pike, was a warning to the others. I wanted them to know we wouldn't stand being treated that way any longer. I'm sure they would have come after me if I had stayed. I left the country soon after to start over where no one knew me."

"It's getting late. I should be heading home soon and I still need to feed. Do you think we could meet again and talk some more?"

Ashleigh smiled, "In the alley across from us here, there's a man… don't feed from him. As for talking again, I would like that. How about we meet up tomorrow night, right here?"

Varruka glanced in the direction of the alley and shrugged. "Sounds like a plan. See you then." She smiled before walking away.

MÀIRI CAMPBELL

Màiri Campbell currently lives in the Pacific Northwest with her husband and their two dogs. She pays homage to both her Celtic and Native American heritage and is active in her local Scottish community. She has been writing since age 10 when one of her poems was locally published. She has since gone onto publishing numerous short stories, a novella, and has a few novels currently in the works. The story A Midnight Meeting is the first in her Forever Fey series. One novel you can follow on her blog and via her newsletter. Her website is www.mairi-campbell.com

A Good Bedtime Story

By

Lucille F. Collazo

My dad was born in 1917, a middle child in a large, tightly knit family. He was very proud of the fact that he had graduated from the "Second Grade" in La Ventana, New Mexico. All his life he loved to read and write poetry, as well as recite poetry from memory. Life was hard back when he was a child and he had to grow up fast working outdoors in northern New Mexico. Those experiences and memories gave him a lot of material for those bedtime stories he loved to tell us.

Some of his stories were about when he was only seven years old and he worked as a sheepherder during the hot summer. He slept beneath the stars and he didn't come home for a month at a time. He earned one dollar for the entire summer, which he gave to his mother. By the time he was twelve years old, he was a cowboy working on his father's ranch and for other ranchers in the area. He often told us stories about Estrella (Spanish for star), his black pony with a white star on its forehead.

I have never forgotten one bedtime story he told us when I was six years old. The four of us children slept on two sets of bunk beds in the same room. There was the boys' side of the room and the girls' side. My younger brother, Tommy, who was two years old and had recently outgrown his crib, was on the lower bunk with a rail so he wouldn't fall off. On the other side of the room were my sister, Sylvia who was four years old and me. We slept together on the lower bunk because we were both afraid of the dark. Our cat, Kitty, slept on the top bunk.

I can still picture Richard in his top bunk that night. His head resting on his arm as he looked down over the edge of his bed at dad who sat on the old wooden rocking chair in the middle of the room. Daddy would rock back and forth for emphasis as he told his story.

This particular story was about a time when he was a young cowboy. He was riding Estrella, on his way back to camp at the end of the day.

"I was enjoying the bright colors of the sun setting on the horizon far away to the west. I was thinking of the dinner I would have when I got back to camp. A cowboy gets real hungry after working hard all day, you know"

Richard asked, "What did you have for lunch, Daddy?"

"Oh probably a nice, thick tortilla with *queso* and some jerky. Anyway, that's what I usually had. Sometimes, if I was lucky, I had dried apples too."

He stopped and was quietly lost in his thoughts for a moment, and then he continued. "It started to get dark, but there was still some light from the sun. All of a sudden I saw a giant walking towards me in the distance. I stopped right there! The giant stopped too! I kicked the sides of my horse gently so he would go forward slowly. The giant didn't get closer, but he was out there. I strained my eyes to make sure I wasn't seeing things...I wasn't! There it was! A giant, bigger than some of the *pinon* trees around me!" Daddy was getting a little excited and that made us listen without interrupting.

"I turned my horse back in the direction I had been coming from. There, right in front of me, at the same distance from me as before, was the same giant! Whoa! I pulled hard on the reins and the pony stopped."

"I didn't know if it was some kind of *brujeria* or witchcraft. I had heard the older men talk about that stuff, witchcraft, around the campfire many evenings after dinner. I was getting kind of scared, so I turned the horse again, in another direction. And right there was the giant again!" Daddy said, "I was scared and nervous and I started to sweat."

He stopped talking for a few seconds and seemed to be thinking about how to continue. After a minute, we all cried, "And then? And then?"

"But, you know, I couldn't figure out why my pony was not nervous or excited like he sometimes acted when there was danger... like when he smelled a mountain lion or a rattle-snake. I sat right there in my saddle, afraid to move. I was thinking, what if there were three or four giants out there? This had never happened to me before."

That scared us. This story was not making me sleepy.

"I took off my hat and wiped my forehead with the back of my hand." Daddy actually did wipe his forehead and after pausing to look at each of our faces, he said, "When I looked up, the giant had disappeared. I looked carefully in all directions. The Giant was gone!"

My sister screamed, "Where did he go?"

Daddy looked at my sister. "The giant? He was gone! I was very happy. So, I put my hat back on." He adjusted the imaginary hat on his head. "And you know what?" Daddy looked to make sure we were still listening. He smiled at us. "The giant was there again! I took my hat off real quick and looked at it." He turned over the imaginary cowboy hat. "There it was... a wrinkled, loose thread hanging down on the front edge of my worn out, old hat." He smiled. "I was so happy when I realized there was no giant! I laughed out loud and pulled off the thread."

As he finished his story, he stood up and smiled. "Now I knew I had a good story to tell the others at camp after dinner."

Tommy had fallen asleep.

Richard laughed with approval. "That was a good one, Daddy! Was it a true story?"

My six-year-old brain was full of questions. I wondered what it would be like to ride a pony all alone in the mountains when it was getting dark. What the pony thought when Dad laughed out loud? And how Daddy found his way back to camp in the dark?

When Daddy finished his story my sister asked for a drink of water, a nightly ritual to avoid going to sleep. Mom came into our room to hear our prayers and tuck us in. Daddy waited by the door and after we blessed everybody we knew, we all took our turns, "Bless me Mama, Bless me Daddy." After we received our blessings, "May God Bless You" from mom and *"Que dios te bendiga"* in Spanish from daddy, lights went out. I remember as I drifted off to sleep, worrying about daddy all by himself in the mountains.

Years later, when I had children of my own, I asked dad if he had made that story up. He was happy to know that I still remembered his bedtime stories and he said, "That one was a true story." He said he never forgot how scared he had been that evening out in the mountains and how happy he was to find the loose thread on his old worn out cowboy hat.

The End

By

Stan Couzens

Lying on the damp, muddy grass, looking at the clearing sky above, I feel a weight on my body. I lie still and try to collect my thoughts.

"What happened?" I'm mumbling words, barely audible, even to me.

A truck goes by; the large all-terrain tires make a low rumble on the broken pavement.

"Help," is all I can manage. Then the sound of vehicles is distant. My ears ring loudly – the result of a nearby explosion. Out of the corner of my eye, there are men walking, poking at other fallen people with their rifles. I glance at the weight holding me down. It is a body. Bloody. The eyes of the corpse, still open, stare at me without seeing. I feel weak – unable to move the heavy man off me.

Finally, a voice in the midst of the movement around me says, "That's it. Let's move out."

The group of men move toward another large truck, mount up, and the engine rumbles away.

I am alone. That is, except for the large man on my chest. As I start clearing the fog from my mind, the strength begins to come back. I move my arms out, and push this dead soldier off me. Able to sit up, I look around and see dozens of other dead soldiers. Some of them are missing parts: arms, legs, and a woman with no head. I double over and empty my stomach. Rising to my feet, I am wobbly and barely able to stand. My feet are partially sunk into the red mud I'm standing in.

"Hello. Hello." I call out to the dead, hoping for one reply. None comes forth. Looking around, I find a helmet, and a rifle. I don't know why I pick it up, but something in my training tells me it is important to have a rifle. I start to walk in the opposite direction of the trucks, guessing that they contained the people responsible for the carnage I leave behind.

I walk until dark, listening to explosions and small arms fire in the distance. I have no idea where I'm going, but I feel I must continue. My canteen is empty and my thirst is worse than the growing hunger in my gut. For the first time since waking up, I check myself over for wounds. Blood is clotted around several small holes in my uniform. Feeling inside, I decide that none of the wounds is life threatening.

I must have been near an explosion. That poor guy on my chest probably got the worst of it. I guess he saved my life. I feel bad that I gave him such an undeserving farewell ceremony. Tears stream down my face.

"What is happening?" I ask the silent trees in the forest. Most of them are without leaves or branches, the end result of bombs, mortars, and machine guns.

"Why was I saved? Why was I the only one to live through all of this?"

"Hey. You're not alone, buddy." A voice comes to me from a nearby bomb hole. "I made it too."

"Me too," chimes another, and another, as soldiers come poking out of numerous holes in the muddy earth around me. We gather, and talk excitedly.

"What unit are you from?" ask several of the bloodied men.

"How long have you been over here?" ask a few others.

Together we find a renewed strength. None of us is alone anymore. We don't have much, but we have each other.

"Who's got rank here?" one of the men asks. We all look around at each other. No one speaks.

"Well, then, who has seniority?" the same man asks.

"Two years, two months," says one man. "But I ain't no officer, and I ain't leading nobody."

"I have three years and eleven months. I guess that makes me the leader." I look down and laugh a little. They all agree.

"Good. Then we'll rest up tonight, and at first light, we'll head out and find a command post somewhere. Agreed?" With that, we all slip back into bomb holes and tree falls. Somebody starts to sing a hymn, softly. I fall asleep.

At first light, I crawl out of the tangle of downed tree branches and stretch. "Okay. Everyone up. Let's get going." There is no response. Going from hole to hole, I look in and find more death, more mangled bodies, and more lifeless eyes staring back at me. I don't understand what happened. Was there another attack last night that I slept through?

Looking up, I see many other soldiers lying on the ground, bloody and lifeless. I rush over to them and shout for anyone to respond. There is no response, nothing.

I see a couple of men near what had been a field hospital. Everyone is dead. One nurse lying with her broken body askew has her head missing. I glance down at a couple of men lying across each other and tears once again stream down my cheeks.

The man on the bottom, staring up, with sightless eyes, is me.

The Beginning

THE GRAY LINE

By

Audrey Van Cleve Dickson

The red dirt road curls around the mound without hesitation continuing for a thousand miles, further than the mind can travel during the dry season. Red pillows of dust float continuously behind the blue Bug, spreading over the treeless grasslands. The noonday sun appears to have conjunctivitis as it stares like a great bloodshot eye into the African afternoon. The Volkswagen lurches and rattles over the corrugated road, sliding and shifting sideways without warning when irritated gravel moves over the washboard surface. At times dust fills the cramped interior, rolling through windows opened against the heat, and oozes from openings in the rusted floor giving the occupants ocher complexions. They taste the bitter, gritty earth, and brace themselves against the rough ride. But on the back seat the baby sleeps in his blue leatherette bed, carefully draped in netting against mosquitoes and tsetse flies.

Up ahead a dark line appears on the road surface. It reaches across the whole of the narrow, lonesome track with no visible beginning or ending. The fatigued car slows to thirty-five miles an hour, moving nearer the apparition. From the passenger side, the mother can see that the line is gray, raised and shaped like a long stick.

"For heaven's sake, slow down!" she yells. Her husband eases on the brakes, cautious against loose gravel.

"It's a snake, a huge snake! I see his head," she shrieks. She holds her breath, but it is too late. They are committed. Thud. As the hot rubber tires bounce over the sinuous serpent, she immediately turns to peer out the rear window hoping for the satisfaction of seeing the immense snake writhing or flattened. "Ohhhhhhhhh!" she breathes.

But behind her the road is empty. There is no line. There is no snake--just a roiling pillar of murram dust wafting over the nodding savanna and the crocodile-skin tire marks in the dirt. Incredulous, she stretches to look again, puzzling, instinctively checking on the baby before settling back into her bucket seat.

"Where could it have gone?" she asks nervously. "How is that possible? Did you see it?" She looks anxiously at him.

He nods and glances quickly into the rear view mirror. Maybe she is irrationally blind and has overlooked it. He remembers how distraught she was when friends discovered the puff adder coiled underneath the burner of the kerosene refrigerator in their kitchen. Now she will not put her hands or feet under a bed or couch without checking first. And since the birth of the baby she checks everything. He can see her hands twisting now; her mouth is tight and thin; a deep dread laces her wide blue eyes. He looks back, again, stares carefully, rationally, scientifically but there is no evidence of a snake on the road. He takes his foot off the gas. As if prompted by some ancient African spirit, they remember this had happened before. They recall the story told to them by long-time expatriates during their first week at work for US AID in East Africa:

A man was traveling alone, driving his small Renault down a gravel road in rural Uganda. Unable to see clearly because of billowing red dust stirred up by an oncoming truck, he did not notice a long thin snake in front of him on the road. He must have heard and felt the bump, of his tires crossing over the snake. But he continued on his journey without stopping, thinking that he had killed the serpent. The snake however was wily. It wrapped itself around the front axle of the car and waited. Later that day, seeking escape, it squeezed through a narrow opening at the base of the clutch petal and entered the car. The man felt something moving inside his pant leg. When he reached down to investigate, the snake bit him. The car was discovered by a passerby, deep in a ditch at the roadside. The man was slumped over the steering wheel, dead of snakebite poisoning. The snake coiled around his neck, was still very much alive.

Suddenly the husband takes decisive action. He stops the car and gingerly gets out. Carefully he kneels down in the thick dust and checks underneath the car, methodically observing each wheel. Nothing looks unusual, just the rusty muffler and undercarriage caked with red murram. As far as he can see, everything looks normal. Satisfied, he claps his hands together, tries to brush the red dust off his khaki pants. He stretches his long slender body to its full six-foot height and searches for any movement in the grasses nearby, but there is none. Pushing his sandy hair out of his pale face, he stands in the dirt tracked road, assessing the situation. Nothing seems amiss. He wishes his beautiful wife would be more rational about things. He feels foolish standing there and tells himself the only reason he stopped was for her.

Since the baby, she wants to go home--back to the USA. Last night in the game park, she thought she heard a big cat outside their tent. She woke him and whispered, "There's a lion or a leopard out there!"

"It's okay. You're just dreaming," he grumped. "Go back to sleep."

But this morning, when she saw huge cat tracks in the damp soil near the tent, she refused to camp again tonight. They had to make reservations in a government rest camp. They are headed there now. He wishes she could be less emotional.

"I thought I saw a slight movement in the back seat," she says looking over her shoulder. A gray line stretches behind the baby's bed in the shadows near his blanket. Her husband remains silent. She knows he probably thinks she is over-reacting.

She cranes her neck, and leans back toward the baby bed. It is nothing really, she thinks, only a shadow. The baby is peacefully sleeping. Nervously, she tells herself everything is okay. Her husband always says she has too active an imagination.

"Everything will be fine," he says. Maybe she should believe him.

This time she is sure she notices something, a slight movement. On the back seat the slithery line is inching forward, upward. Now she sees piercing red eyes. They are staring at her from atop the blue leatherette bed. Now they are under the mosquito netting. She glances at the baby. He is still, except for the rise and fall of his little chest.

For an instant she freezes, knowing that one wrong move could cost her baby's life. From its appearance she knows that the dark skinny snake is not a constrictor. Most likely it is a Mamba, mean, venomous, fast as lightening. Lifting her left hand she starts a slow rhythmic movement like she once saw snake charmers use in India. She hopes to distract the snake, keep his attention away from the baby. Her hand waves side to side. The movement holds the gaze of the red-eyed menace. He sees her moving, advances under the net to the outside of the bed, his head lifted toward her. Silently, with her right hand, she signals to her husband not to say anything or move.

Her eyes are riveted on the snake whose penetrating orbs are still watching her movements as he rises above the netting. His black forked tongue is flicking in and out of his sinister mouth, testing the air for scents he recognizes. She knows she must capture his attention, keep him coming toward her. Her left hand continues to wave slowly back and forth.

Instinctively, with her right hand, she grabs for something to defend herself. There is the sound of shattering glass. Hearing the noise, the snake suddenly lunges forward. She screams. The car skids to a halt just as the long gray snake's body flips over the driver's seat, twists over the father's head. Terrified, he glances at his wife in time to see her lashing something at the venomous creature.

"My God," he groans, "you have pinned the viper down on the drive shaft hump!" The snake's head, all but severed, is firmly wedged inside a broken baby bottle. The red eyes are bulging. With all her might and determination, she holds him down with the gouged edge of the broken bottle. The snake stops writhing.

"Is he dead yet?" she asks weakly.

"Yes! How did you do that?" He reaches out, encircling her in his arms

"I have no idea," she says, sobbing.

Just then, the baby awakens from the commotion, and sets up a loud screaming cry. She turns, scoops him up and rocks him back and forth in her arms.

Exactly one week later to the day, mother, father and baby boy, board a 707 jet bound for New York City.

RUDY'S DREAM

By

D.M. Dubay

The dull fabric of the old J-3 Cub, ripped and faded, flapped in the breeze. Rudy didn't remember if the plane had a propeller or engine. He remembered only how beautiful it looked tied down behind their house and how much he wished it were his very own.

When tall enough to sit in its cockpit and reach the rudder pedals, Rudy spent hours pretending to fly. Whenever southwesterly winds picked up, he rushed out to lengthen the tie-down ropes so the plane would lift off momentarily in a gust. He knew, even as a child, that wings would produce lift with a strong wind and the plane would become airborne unless tied down.

Sitting at the controls, he moved them forward and aft, left and right. By the time he was eleven, he had more *flight time* than many pilots have in a lifetime. Sometimes his best friend Jimmy sat in the front seat and Rudy *instructed* him. They took turns handling the controls.

Rudy's dad, a pilot, recognized his son's love of flying. He knew he would need money for flying lessons so, when Rudy turned thirteen, he taught him how to trap. "By next winter you'll be able to run trap lines yourself using the snow machine to check them. Any money you make above expenses can be saved for flying lessons. By the time you're fifteen, you should have enough for a private pilot certificate. Does that sound fair?"

"Sure, Dad, and maybe Jimmy can help."

Excitement and responsibility kept the boys focused. The beaver, muskrat, and mink they trapped were easy to release when they checked the trap line on Saturdays. Most had frozen in the traps. Over the next two years, they sold enough pelts to more than cover their meager expenses, and because Rudy saved most of what he earned, he had enough for flying lessons by the time he was fifteen.

One February day, while passing a private airstrip after checking traps, Rudy noticed a ski plane tied down there. He drove closer to check it out.

Jimmy hung on behind him.

"Wow, cool!" Jimmy said. "Maybe we can get in to get a closer look."

"We'd better not, Jimmy, this is private property, remember. We probably shouldn't even be here. But it is really cool."

As they stopped to admire the plane, a grey-bearded man in heavy duck Carharts and Sorrel boots walked up behind them and growled, "She's a beauty, isn't she? How would you boys like to fly her?"

Rudy and Jimmy were too stunned to speak. They expected to be in trouble. Instead they were offered the chance of a lifetime.

"I run the engine once in a while to keep it lubricated, and figure I may as well fly it rather than wasting fuel."

They all squeezed into the plane. Once airborne, the old man, Gustaf, let Rudy take the controls.

"Where did a young whippersnapper like you learn to fly?"

Rudy fibbed, "Oh, I've been flying for a long time. Dad runs a flying service."

After landing and parking the plane, eager to fly again, Rudy asked if they could come back and exchange work for flying time.

"Oh, I don't own the plane," Gustaf said. "I'm just watching it for a guy who's looking to sell it."

"Sell it?"

"Yup, the owner's desperate for cash."

Rudy's mind raced. *Maybe Dad could buy it for me to take lessons in… or maybe…* his face lit up with an exciting idea.

Gustaf continued, "Anyway, it's a great way to check my traps from the air. You'd be amazed how much ground you can cover in a jiffy. Stop by anytime. If it's still here, we'll go for a ride."

"Wow, that'd be great." Rudy grinned. "Thanks a bunch."

Rudy daydreamed of handling the controls again. He dreamed of owning the plane. Even racing across frozen lakes at full throttle on the snow machine didn't hold the same thrill as flying. He visualized zooming over the treetops sending moose running. He *had* been flying for a long time, with his father at the controls. Now he wanted to be in charge.

The plane was not on the airstrip the following week. "Darn it, Jimmy, maybe he sold it." Rudy's shoulders sagged. He dragged himself through his classes for the next two weeks, convinced he had missed the opportunity to buy the plane. Money he had secretly withdrawn from savings was burning a hole in his pocket.

The next time they passed the airstrip on the way to check their traps, there she was. It looked like Gustaf was ready to take off. Rudy raced to the airstrip, kicking up snow as he swung alongside the taxiing plane. Jimmy hung on with one arm, waving frantically. Just as they were ready to give up, the plane slowed and came to a stop in the middle of the airstrip.

Before the propeller finished winding down, a stranger jumped out, shaking his fist and yelling, "What in the hell are you doing? Do you want to get us killed? Hasn't anyone explained to you the dangers of being near a plane taking off? I've got a mind to haul you both in to town and report you to the sheriff for trespassing. Now get your butts off this strip before I throw you off!"

Rudy squared his shoulders and took a deep breath. "Now, sir, I just wanted to make sure nobody was stealing my plane. It looked like you were about to take off with her."

"Your plane? Hah! This is *my* old beat... aah... beauty, kid. And, what the hell, you couldn't own a plane anyway, you're just a kid."

"I told Gustaf I wanted to buy it. In fact, I brought along $2,500 today to sew up the deal." Rudy hoped for an opportunity to make an offer on the plane. He didn't know how much, but he'd overheard his father talking about an old two-place plane, a Taylor-craft he'd bought for parts for $1,500. He thought $2,500 for an operational plane might be about right. With false bravado he reached into his pocket and pulled out twenty-five one hundred dollar bills.

"Are you the owner, sir?" Rudy asked. "If so, we can settle this right here."

Jimmy made choking sounds and Rudy elbowed him in the ribs as he said to the man, "Just sign over the title to me and it's a done deal."

At the sight of the money, the man's attitude changed. "Sure, kid, why don't we just head inside and talk it over." They walked to the small shed alongside the strip. "I've got to get back to Anchorage pretty quick, though. Look, I've got the title right here. I can sign it over, then you can fly me up to Anchorage." He grinned like a fox discovering a hole in the chicken coop. Pocketing the money, the guy said, "Okay, let's get a move on. It'll be getting dark soon. Time's a wasting."

Rudy's heart pounded, but he couldn't admit he didn't know how to fly. His mind raced. *How am I going to get the plane back here? What will*

I tell my dad? What about the trap line? I don't even know if the plane has a radio.

Outwardly, he was calm and collected. "Now, Jimmy, you finish running the line. Come back and pick me up around seven. I should be back by then."

Pulling him aside, Rudy whispered to Jimmy, "Don't tell anyone anything until we have a chance to get our stories straight. We'll think of something."

Jimmy looked like he would cry and Rudy shoved him in the chest, "Come on, Jimbo, we're in this together. Think of the fun we'll have!"

Rudy turned and hopped into the plane. Relieved to see the previous owner in the pilot seat, he relaxed. *I'll figure it out.* He concentrated so hard on trying to remember everything the pilot did, he hardy heard his animated conversation.

The pilot shouted above the noise, "Yeah ... good old bird ... little TLC. I was gonna put her on sale ... Lake Hood ... lucky for you ... first. My buddy will be flabbergasted ... tough times ... the Slope ... no money to support ... airplane ... other habits, ha-ha. Lots of fun ... miss her."

Something in the guy's voice and manner made Rudy uncomfortable, but the thought of owning the airplane overshadowed it. The man talked about his trips with the plane. Narrow escapes and bad weather encounters were laughed off as a normal part of flying in Alaska.

Before Rudy knew it, they were crossing Turnagain Arm and soon descended toward a small airstrip. "We'll land at O'Malley strip. I left my car there."

Rudy was glad about that. He was accustomed to bush airstrips, flying with his dad. He knew O'Malley strip had no control tower and very few airplanes.

The guy flew over the airstrip to check the windsock. A fresh layer of snow made it difficult to recognize the edges of the strip, but parked airplanes defined one side.

"Not much of a wind, kid. You can take off to the north after I turn her around. If you don't mind, we'll just leave the engine running. I'll jump out, so you can take right off and get back to Kenai before dark." He sounded eager to get away.

"Yeah, great." *Lucky he can't tell how nervous I am.* The man landed the plane with a thud, causing Rudy to bite his tongue. He taxied to a wide spot at the end of the strip near a red Corvette and turned the airplane around.

"Been a real pleasure dealing with you, kid. If you ever wanna see some action around town, give me a call. I know some hot chicks for a good time, if you know what I mean." He shook Rudy's hand and jumped out. "Next time!" He bounded away from the plane.

Rudy slid left and buckled in, eager to get away. He pushed the throttle forward tentatively. The skis stuck to the snow-covered runway for a moment and then broke free. Rudy was committed. Looking down the runway, he noticed the plane veering left toward the trees. Instinctively, with all his might, he turned the control yoke to the right. Nothing happened. As the plane was about to go off the left side of the runway, he remembered his dad saying something about steering with rudders. He stomped on the right rudder. The plane lurched to the right and then left again as Rudy reversed controls. His left hand tightened on the yoke and he pulled back as the plane neared the trees for the second time. Suddenly he was airborne. "Yahoo, I'm flying!"

The trees surrounding the runway brushed by as Rudy tightened his grip on the yoke. But something didn't feel right. The plane wasn't climbing like it should. A horn was blaring in Rudy's ear. *Oh, man. I can't do anything right. What's happening?* His hand relaxed on the yoke and the airplane began to climb. *Okay, better. Now, let's get her turned around. I'll keep the mountains on my left, cross the inlet, then follow the shoreline. That should take me back home. I'll recognize Johnson's Road from the air and the strip is right at the end of it.* Rudy looked around. He noticed large jets approaching Anchorage International Airport. *I'd better stay low and out of their way.*

The inlet looked much wider than it had on the trip north. Rudy looked at his watch. *Man, it's already five-thirty. I didn't think it was so late. When does it get dark? Don't know, but I must have plenty of time. It can't take much more than an hour to get back to Kenai.*

When he came to the south shore, he turned west and flew over the shoreline. The westerly wind increased and his groundspeed decreased dramatically. He felt like he was suspended in midair. After what seemed like an eternity, he reached Point Possession and turned south toward Kenai. *Now I'm home free. I'll be home in no time.* But the wind turned into a quartering headwind and his groundspeed was little better than it had been when heading west. He looked at his watch again. *Six fifteen! Wow, that took a long time. I wonder how much gas is in this thing.* Looking around inside the plane for the first time since taking off, he couldn't find any gas gauges. *Well, there must be enough.*

The sun neared the horizon. Nothing looked familiar. Flying at less than five hundred feet above the snow-covered terrain, he couldn't tell frozen lakes from swampy areas. They all looked the same.

What have I gotten into? Well, I'll just have to keep the shore in sight and keep going. I'd certainly recognize the Kenai River. If I see it, I'll know I went too far and turn around. This comforted him for a while. He glanced at his watch again: six forty-five. Deepening twilight lengthened the shadows, making Rudy struggle to identify landmarks. *At least it's a clear day.*

Just then, the engine made a sputtering sound and Rudy grabbed the yoke more tightly. Sweat ran down his face in spite of the cold air blowing in around the windows. He noticed another knob next to the throttle labeled "heat." He pulled it hoping to get some warm air. The engine noise got worse, and he was tempted to reverse what he had done. *No, I'll leave it on. I need heat. I want to be warm if I crash.*

Spasms gripped his stomach as he looked for something familiar. In his fear, he had climbed a little higher and with a wider perspective he could identify some buildings.

Aloud, in his excitement, he said, "Whoa! There's the Radcliff's fishing cabin. Yeah, right! There's the wrecked boat on the beach. I know where I am. Yahoo!" The engine noise smoothed out and Rudy breathed a sigh of relief. He turned the airplane around—circling higher and higher—looking for Johnson's road and the airstrip. His throat was dry and his head hurt.

Even though his dad was not in the plane with him, he imagined him there. "I don't know what to do, Dad." Tears welled up. Fear of punishment added to his anguish. *But, Daddy is always fair. He always helps me out of scrapes.* He could almost hear his dad's soothing voice giving him advice. *Stay calm, Rudy. Think. What are the positives?*

These words always helped him before. Maybe they could help him now. He took a deep breath and focused. *What are the positives? Well, I'm still airborne. I sort of know where I am. The engine is running... weather is good. The wind has died.* With each positive statement, his thinking cleared. His confidence returned.

What else did Dad always say? What is the question? Use your head. Don't rely on feelings or get discouraged. Okay, now. The question is how to find the airstrip. He scratched his chin. I know! I can fly a grid pattern.

He flew back to the beach and located the wrecked boat on the shore. *I know the airstrip is about two miles east of the shoreline and I figure it's a little south of the wreck. I'll fly east for a couple minutes, then turn right and fly west to the shore and then repeat until I see Johnson's Road.*

On making his first turn back to the west he noticed lights of a moving vehicle on the ground. They went straight for a while, circled around, then straight in the opposite direction. He flew closer to the moving light. It was a snow machine racing along a wide-open expanse of white. *It must be Jimmy. Bless his soul! He's showing me the strip.*

Rudy wagged the wings and turned around to get lined up with the airstrip, its faint outline barely discernible in the semi-darkness. Light from the snow machine continued to define the landing area. Rudy tried to remember exactly what his dad did when approaching to land. He remembered him bringing the throttle to idle and using the trim wheel. *Where is the trim wheel in this thing? No time to look right now.*

It was getting more difficult to keep the airplane in a level flight attitude. Rudy pulled harder and harder on the yoke as the plane lost altitude and settled towards the ground. Before he realized it, he was over the airstrip still moving too fast. He clenched his teeth and braced for impact. Halfway down the strip, the plane settled onto the snow. At first Rudy didn't realize he had landed. Although the snow covered runway slowed him a little, the skis were slippery and he sped by the snow machine with its lights on. The snow berm at the end of the strip loomed closer. Rudy pulled the mixture control aft as his dad did when approaching the shoreline in a floatplane. The engine quit. The propeller stopped. Now all he could do was hang on and wait for the momentum of the airplane to slow.

As though in slow motion, he hit the berm. The airplane began to tip up onto its nose. He thought it might flip over completely, but was powerless to do anything. He was along for the ride. The plane came to a stop in an almost vertical position with the propeller and spinner wedged in the snow bank. Rudy's blood pounded in his ears. Hanging by his seat belt, he reached to open the door and grab the doorframe. He released his belt, braced his feet against the instrument panel and jumped to the ground.

Jimmy stood there, wide-eyed. "Gee whiz! I thought you were going to kill yourself."

Rudy laughed hysterically. Relief washed over him and the sight of the airplane with its nose stuck in the snow struck him as hilarious.

"What a blast, Jimmy! I got me a plane."

D.M. DUBAY

D.M. Dubay lives in the Pacific Northwest with her husband, Bud. When not writing she spends time tending their small vineyard with him and landscaping their property, hiking with their children and two granddaughters, singing with multiple chorale groups and volunteering as a spiritual director.

She spent years exploring the Last Frontier, Alaska, as a professional pilot. Now, a retired Northwest Airlines international pilot, she flies her own plane for pleasure. Her love of flying and the great outdoors permeates her novels as well as her poetry. In her writing D.M. Dubay illustrates the importance of faith, hope and love.

Three Poems

By

Serena DuBois

Serena DuBois

A Leaf's Story

I've had a good life.

I've sucked in CO2 and shoved out oxygen,
helping Mama grow big and strong.

I've joined my many siblings in shading the yard,
while those weird creatures moved
freely past me,

My sister says, "It's time to go."
We must move on to ...
To what?
Where will I go?
What's next for me?

Oh! Here comes a breeze.
I'm dancing,
dancing.

The breeze grows stronger.
Snap!

I'm off, flying with the wind.
There's the dwelling where those
creatures disappear.

And over here—more trees.
A new home.

The wind drops me,
Lets me go.

I settle in around an old tree's roots.

And there's my brother beside me.
    I see
        A new life coming.

Serena DuBois

Freight Train

When I was young, I watched the Mallet-engined trains
rumble slowly
Through my sleepy railroad town,
Gradually building speed as they headed eastward
out and up into Sierras high.

My days were long and slow
moving with the rhythm of those old, slow freights.
Each hour seemed a day,
Each day a year
And years stretched onward to infinity.

But now it seems my life-train builds up speed
and each spring flashes by like sleepy hamlets
here and gone again.

At times I long to scream out, "Halt!"
Flash red lights and bring back
those lingering days of youth.

But vision comes of speed so great
my engine crashes past the barriers of life
And my soul
Derailed
Flies free
To find at last
Eternity.

JANUARY 31, 1942

A war was beginning
As I came rushing into the world.

The story goes
    My parents had been out for an evening,
    After coming home, Mother, standing, ironing at 2 AM.
        Suddenly said,
            "George, my water broke."

My Uncle Jack told me the tale.
    They rushed his sister by taxi to
        Alta Bates Hospital, Berkeley, Cal.

An hour and a half later I was born
    into a war-torn world.

Six months later the world at war hit home.
    My parents were divorcing.
    My father had enlisted.
        My sister and I were living with our grandparents,
            Far from Berkeley and the war.

I remember my father back from a German prison camp,
    Thin,
    Still in uniform,
        Visiting my grandparents' home.

But mostly I remember my grandparents caring for me
        Far from Berkeley and the war.

Poetry

By

Arlene Sundquist Empie

Arlene Sundquist Empie

Destination: Fishtown

Paddles up. Forward. Portside paddles not quite in synch. Rest.
The silent river current carries minds and bodies gently onward.
I lean to look at underwater plant growth, silt-covered branches
barely visible beneath the surface at low tide, suspended like
uncle John Vincent's body in the arms of the Skagit.

A passel of poets or poetic pullers in the black Salish Dancer,
red interior, wolf-like decorative bow like a Coastal Salish canoe.
Destination: Fishtown's old shacks and landings at the mouth of
the Skagit, that decades ago held the musings and creative arts
of LaConner's colony of hippies.

Rain falling in vertical torrents, trickling down mounds
      of glistening blue, red and yellow slickers
      wielding wood paddles.
Raindrops piercing,
      penetrating the cold steel surface
      of The River.
Rain bouncing skyward like sparkling diamonds,
      like a school of searun trout breaking the surface
      of their native river to feed on raindrops.

Swinomish gillnetters look up to ponder what the heck are these
white guys doing, paddling down the Skagit in pouring rain. Bald
eagle soars and circles, quizzically eyeing the unusual sight of
canoes full of colorful raingear, rafted together under nascent dark
clouds. Is eagle, too, listening to poetry on the river?

Where exactly is Fishtown now, except for a state of mind?
The River branches into Steamboat Slough; we paddle sharp
right into Sullivan Slough, past Smuggler's Cove before heading
toward Fish Hole break in the jetty to reach Swinomish Slough.
We silently paddle forward.

If not for the rain, would 32 pullers slip into Robert Sund's old
net shack on Shit Creek, or more kindly Disappearing Lake,
to sip steaming hot cups of tea brewed by the caretaker artist?
Mindful of Sund's presence, I listen, as his poetic words meet up
again with weathered wood walls.

The warmth of a rusted cast-iron stove crackling with split dry
alder dims the ravages and dampness of paddling in torrents of
rain. My imagination gives way to the thought of 32 people
within a ten by twelve shack nestled among reeds, resting on
decaying wood piers, enough so to think it might be swaying,

just a little. If Sund's shack should succumb, legions of
Robert Sund's followers and friends would never forgive or
forget the extravagance of a few poets on a rainy day whose
elation for just being there will forever remain.

Arlene Sundquist Empie

Dunlins Beside the Salish Sea

I walk Padilla Bay dike to hear thousands of dunlins,
shorebirds in motion, swirling in synchronized flight, the
sweetness of their calls a dunlin symphony. The soft, numinous
sound of an orchestral masterpiece that brings forth disturbing
emotions like 'the little phrase' Proust identified, a combination
of notes with the power to open and change the soul space.

Dunlins ply the shoreline, settle at the edge of the Salish Sea
pointy beaks pick at delicacies brought by the incoming tide.

As abruptly as they swoop to water's edge, the flock
rises as one being and continues their extravagant display.
A cloud of dunlins sweeps by me, the whole flock turning
like an abstract expressionist's brush spreads black paint
a magnificent swoop across a grey canvas, suddenly to
reverse the gesture with a wide stroke of white.

Dark-feathered dunlins rise and fall, turn abruptly to reveal
white underbellies, the once-dark cloud becomes whiteness.

I recall the day I walked the trail to where the dunlins play
—not a dunlin in sight. The estuary, gleaming mud flats
the channel, a curvilinear path carved in silt sans seawater.
Why hadn't I checked the tidal chart? Disappointment walked
with me as I slowly retraced my steps toward the trailhead.
I talked to the dunlins or was it the universe?

I long to see you, to hear you, to feel my chest
swell with feelings that uplift body and soul.

I hear them coming, southward from the sea, flying low,
somewhat in a line, coming straight up Indian Slough.
The sweetness of their chorus crescendos as they flock
together, turn, circle around me, and fly back to the sea.

Poetry by Arlene Sundquist Empie

A Midsummer Night in Finland

My thoughts return to Grisselö cove beside the Baltic Sea
where mirror images in still water meet old and new boats
where Bengt moors his seaworthy wooden sailboat,
a replica of centuries-old workboats, finely crafted by
hands shaping sculptural ribs, tending the joinery, rigging
the spar. Wind and oars propelled our ancestral fishers out
into the open sea, sometimes tragically not to return.

This is the place, he muses as his gaze crosses the sea
where grandfather launched a similar craft in 1890
calloused farmer's hands pulling oars, gaffs set, unfurling
a single sail in the wood boat, reaching along the coast.
Then, a one-way crossing by wind and oars to Sweden
where he embarks on his ocean journey to America.

Silence is palpable on a midsummer eve in Finland.
I envision a sail amidst the cloudbank on the horizon.
An orange midnight sun streaks across the serene sea
silhouettes a sauna hut on a point jutting into the bay.
There are no words as Bengt and I stand on weathered
planks of an old dock quietly pondering time and place.

In each other's eyes, mirror images of past and present
a faint glint of ancestors and the future before us separated
by ocean and continents. Mist obscures our personal journeys.

ARLENE SUNDQUIST EMPIE:

Author of four award-winning poetry and non-fiction books: Love Is A Place, Minding A Sacred Place, and The Legacy of Ida Lillbroända published in Finland under Swedish title Till Amerika vi gå. She exudes pride and passion in her Nordic roots and cultural heritage and is a Board Trustee, Nordic Heritage Museum. Born and raised in Skagit Valley, Sunnie's deep love of Nature and place inspires a new venture as lingonberry grower on her 12-acre Sundquist Farm*Garden. Bachelor of Arts, The Evergreen State College 1980; professional accordionist with Hugo's Accordion Band and Leif, Lena & Lars trio.

Cowboy's Luck

By

M.B. Frazier

I 'm Pete Collins. I'm middle-aged and I consider myself a good all-around cowboy. My gelding, Apache, is the best cutting horse in the territory.

Standing near the spring where I camped last night, I look down on a rambling ranch in the valley below. I've been traveling two weeks looking for work as a cowhand. So far I've had no luck. "This ranch could turn my luck around, Apache." I throw my saddle on his back.

"Better clean up a bit before riding down there. Don't want them to think I'm a bum, do we, Apache?"

Bending down, I cup cold water in my hands and splash it across my face. I run wet fingers through my graying hair and put on my black cowboy hat. This old friend has seen me through many a hard time. "Hope this won't be another one," I mumble.

I mount Apache and ride on down to the corral and dismount. Before I open the gate I notice a tall blonde woman standing at the barn door holding a rifle. It's aiming right at me. "You sure are pretty, but that rifle ain't," I stutter holding my breath.

"Don't take kindly to strangers sneakin' up on me. You better be quick to tell me what you want, or get back on your horse and ride out 'fore I put a bullet in ya!"

I don't know how to handle this situation, but I have to try. "Whoa lady, will you please put that gun down? I'm not here to harm you, I just rode in to see if you need any help workin' them cattle in the pasture over yonder."

She hesitates, and then lowers the gun.

I let out a long breath and say, "Thank you ma'am."

She sizes me up. "I'm just a plain old cowhand lookin' for work, ma'am. To my surprise she invites me up to the porch for a bite to eat, but keeps the gun handy.

"My name is Sara Downey. What's yours?"

"You read my mind, Miss Downey, I was just gonna ask your name.

I'm Pete Collins."

"My brother Caleb and I own the ranch. He comes out from the city at brandin' time. He went to town looking for hands to hire. I expect him back any time now."

"Looks like I might be in the right place. Do you or your brother do the hirin'?"

"I'm the boss."

"Yes ma'am, "I take my hat off, "Be a pleasure to work for you ma'am."

"Call me Sara. Come on up to the house and I'll get you some grub."

Walking towards the farmhouse, I notice what must be a bunkhouse off to my left. I mutter to myself, "I like this place. Be a good place to spend the winter. A feller would do right by spendin' the rest of his days here."

"What's that?" She asks, "Did you say something?"

I reply, "No, just thinkin'."

"Come up on the porch, sit on the bench, and I'll bring you a bowl of stew and a cup of coffee."

Sara disappears into the house and returns with a large bowl of stew and a steaming-hot cup of coffee.

"This stew tastes so good, ma'am, thank you." I gulp the coffee down. "Can you spare another cup of coffee?"

Sara fixes me with a steady gaze that lifts the weight from my shoulders. She goes into the kitchen, and returns with another cup of coffee. She sees Caleb and two men ride in. "Maybe now we can get some work done around here!"

"How many hands do you need?"

"I'm hiring you and those two others and there's plenty of stew for everyone."

After the meal, we go outside to discuss work plans for the next day. Outside, Caleb says he doesn't appreciate ranch life like Sara does. He says Sara grew up on this ranch. She knows no other life, and must make a go of it, but he wants to return to the city as soon as possible.

I think to myself, "Sure would like to be the cowboy that fills your boots."

Sara and I walk awhile longer checking the stock, feeding the horses, and bedding down the chickens while shadows lengthen. We watch the crescent moon rise on the horizon until Sara says, "I'm hitting the hay. Tomorrow comes early here." I wait until I see the kitchen is dark before I head to the bunkhouse.

Four in the morning, the triangle on the porch of the main house clangs. All three of us men in the bunkhouse know it is time to rise and shine. I pull on my boots, wash my hands, and splash cold water on my face from the basin outside the door. I'm ready for the day.

Breakfast is served in the kitchen of the main house. Being the first to arrive, I pour myself a cup of coffee and sit down next to a window overlooking the corral and out buildings. "This is one nice setup you have here and the grub is good too," I say, as Sara comes into the kitchen, stokes the stove, and adds firewood.

"I like it! Beautiful day isn't it Pete?" Sara smiles broadly, fixing grub.

"Yes ma'am and that herd down there is some of the best lookin' stock I've ever seen."

"They're Herefords. Dad bred this line back when he homesteaded."

"Well they're a mighty fine lookin' bunch."

"You know anything 'bout breedin' cattle?"

"A little, but looks like you know how to run this ranch and the cowhands. Before long with your sweet smile, we'll be bendin' over backwards to please you."

Caleb and the other two cowhands join us. Sara tosses the grub on the table." You boys sit down now, and get your bellies full 'fore goin' out to work."

Meal over, I leave the house with the other cowhands and Sara is left alone with Caleb.

"What a nice, polite, good lookin' guy Pete is, Caleb. He and I think alike, guess I'll keep him around for a while."

"You're the boss. Do what you want. I'll be leaving soon."

"Yeah, I know. I've been lookin' for someone to take your place. This could be the cowboy."

"Suits me fine."

Sara finishes her household chores, feeds the chickens, slops the hogs, and saddles Mollie. She rides out to check on the hands.

Pete sees her coming and grins, "Nice to see you boss.

Sara nods. "Good to see you too, Pete."

Poetry by Benson Harer

By

Benson Harer

THE SMOKING PORCH

The man, religious in all respects, rocks in the beat-up lounge chair.
Padded in beige linen, it was discarded from the house, to be useful
As a luxury for the smokers, banned from indoors. It is good as a place
To recollect and ponder on the nuances of humanity and winds of nature,
As his life in America means struggling to maintain calm.
His rosary sits in his lap, sky blue beads highlighting its cross.
He ponders his commute to the Catholic church each day.
For a ceremony at eleven, when he prays for peace and questions existence.
Snowy gray hair contrasts with his dark Hispanic skin.
Silently, the sun shines around the shade of the canopy of the smoking porch.

Feeling of Age

I am young but I am old.
Not as young as I wish.
But I'd rather not
Turn back the clock.
For I'd rather not face
The choice I'd have to make.

Guardian

A guard at my back
As I may fall again.
I stand with support
And thus, it lies before me.
Behind me.
Coming to me.
Passing by me.
I catch what I can at fleeting moments
And I stand honorably
With a deep love
And hide,
Trusting fate.

Pencil and Paper

By

Jaana Hatton

My head is heavy with words again. Like an apple tree in September, it needs to be harvested, but how do I record these fruits of my mind? Should I use machinery, such as my computer, or remain old-fashioned, writing by hand?

It is not such a difficult choice: I love pencil and paper. Writing words on a fresh sheet is like a chat with a dear friend. The easy familiarity makes conversation comfortable. Paper and wood, remnants of nature, still have the soft breath of life in them, tiny souls that mirror mine.

The motions of my hand shake the stray thoughts free from my bursting brain. They bounce into the graphite and finally settle down on the page. On occasion, they may even make sense. Babbling or brilliance, those strokes will stay where I placed them. It is rarely so with computers.

It's often downright aggravating to peck at the keyboard. Using that tabloid of torture, the tips of my fingers hurt after a few minutes. My wrists ache and my shoulders stiffen. The constant tapping sound soon becomes as irritating as a woodpecker. There is no comforting sense of conversation, only the pounding pulse of irritation.

Then, in my enthusiasm, I mistakenly press some mysterious key. The elaborate, brilliant paragraphs swiftly disappear! They vanish somewhere inside the devilish machine. How I wish those lovely lines had been written down on solid paper!

Yes, I love my simple pencil and the worn notebook. Peaceful pages await my greeting. There is no dull, gray screen staring at me with the restless little blinker. Oh, thou blessed sheets of serenity!

Beach Essentials

By

Leslie J. Heineman

The roomy canvas bag of beach essentials hung off her right shoulder as Anna left her aunt and uncle's house alone. Her hands were pushed into the front pockets of her cutoffs; her brilliant blue eyes were hidden behind the new Ray-Bans her mother had given her when she turned seventeen only weeks before. Now, she gazed only at the gritty pavement; her other senses were immune to the heady saltwater-drenched air, the distant roar of waves crashing on the shore.

The morning sun warmed her back as she walked slowly along the now-familiar path. Pacific Coast Highway—PCH, as she, like the locals, had come to call it—lay ahead. The sun's slanting rays bounced off the cars moving unhurriedly north and south. *People going to work,* she thought. *It must be nice to be all grown up, to have somewhere important to be at this hour of the day.*

"Where are you going?" her aunt Karen had asked earlier as Anna prepared a piece of toast and gulped a small glass of orange juice. Karen was on her second cup of coffee and, most likely, her second or third cigarette. "You remember that your mother is having surgery today, don't you?"

"Of course," Anna said, more flippantly than she would have dared with her own mother. But she and her once-favorite aunt were on shaky ground. It seemed clear to Anna that she, her little brother, Robbie, and her cancer-riddled mother had seriously overstayed their welcome.

Her mother had surprised them with the two-week California vacation at the end of the school year; three weeks later, no one seemed to know just when they could return home to the cool, green Northwest. Anna had done her best to help with household chores—cooking, cleaning, and keeping up with three people's laundry—but nothing she did seemed good enough. Just the day before, Karen had found her sorely lacking in the bathroom-cleaning department. Anna kicked at an empty Coke can as she walked along the busy road. *I'm sick and tired of her inspections and her interrogations every time I leave the house.*

At the entrance to the beautiful state beach, gulls screeched and a dozen or so early-risers jogged along the foamy edge of the oceanfront Anna had grown to love. Beaches along Puget Sound were more rocky than sandy; the water was icy and lapped at the gray rocks and driftwood-strewn strand. Here, the silky, nearly white sand was "vacuumed" every evening to scoop up unsightly trash, and so squeaky hot at midday that she had to protect the bottoms of her feet with her new blue thongs.

Anna smoothed out her towel on a patch of level sand and sat with her long tawny legs stretched out before her. Only weeks before they had been as pasty white as the sheets she put on her bed. Now she admired the new sun-kissed skin she shaved and oiled every day, indulging in the California sun for the first time. She knew she turned heads in the land of surfers and polka-dot bikinis. She had inherited the tall, slender frame of her Scandinavian father and the wavy brown hair of her mother; three weeks of walking the beach and swimming in the ocean had firmed her body and tanned her skin as never before.

Anna lay back, letting the sand's warmth seep through the worn terry cloth and into her tense back muscles. At that moment, a surgeon was cutting her mother open to see what hadn't been detectable with x-rays, ultrasounds, and palpitations. After months of grueling chemo and radiation, and two major surgeries to remove the cancer, something had gone terribly wrong. Instead of the rest and healing her mother had expected on this trip, pain and swelling again wracked her core, and the local doctor recommended immediate surgery. *What would they find?* Anna wondered, only slightly aware of the distant roar of the waves and children squealing as they played somewhere up the strand. Her eyes closed, and her mind stilled as she soaked up the sun.

Suddenly, a shadow fell across her face, waking Anna from a soothing dream of the cool woods near her home. She opened her eyes to see Karen and Robbie standing over her.

"What time is it?" She struggled to get up.

"It's noon," Karen said. "We haven't heard from you all morning, so we thought we'd better come find you."

"I can't believe I fell asleep!" Anna said. "Can you take me to the hospital now?"

"Yes," Karen said. "I'll drop you off first then I have to get a few things at the store. I'll take Robbie with me." At 11, Robbie wasn't allowed in the surgical unit, so he depended on Anna for news of their mother's condition. He bent to help Anna gather up her things, and the three of them walked hurriedly and clumsily toward Karen's yellow sedan.

Karen seemed angry about something as she drove along PCH. Ignoring her aunt's apparent pique, Anna gripped her armrest and watched the scenery whiz by—the power plant, the pier and tourist shops, and the tiny breakfast joint that her uncle Hank had taken her and Robbie to one day after they had first arrived. Now, she just wanted to go back to that happier time when they were all optimistic about her mother's chances. What would happen to her and Robbie if Mother didn't make it this time?

As Karen pulled up to the front entrance of the hospital, an imposing boxlike structure on Beach Boulevard, Anna grabbed her still-sandy bag from the back seat and paused to look at Karen and then Robbie. "Thanks. When will you be back?"

"I'm not sure, but our errands shouldn't take too long."

"Okay ... see you in a while." She stepped out into the bright midday sun and walked slowly, yet resolutely, through the revolving door without a backward glance.

Someone at the nurses' station directed her to the room. Anna walked down the lonely corridor of the surgical unit to see her mother. It was quiet in the hallway and in the room before her. The pounding of her heart was the only sound as she reached for the door.

She wasn't prepared for what she saw.

Her mother was alone in a two-bed room. Anna stood riveted to the floor just inside the door as she took in the scene. Her mother's wasted body made a slight ridge lengthwise under the single sheet that covered her. Tubing of various sizes disappeared into every orifice—oxygen pumped through her nose into her lungs, a rubber NG tube also passed through her nose to her stomach, a catheter collected urine. An assortment of beeping, blinking machines monitored her vitals. Clear fluid dripped hypnotically from a bag hanging next to her bed, through a tube and a needle that disappeared under the bruised skin of her right arm. Her thin arms lay next to her atop the sheet, the skin like ancient, yellowed parchment with multicolored bruises where someone had stuck her with a needle or lifted her too vigorously. Anna's eyes swiveled to her mother's face, which looked ghoulish and unfamiliar. Her sparse black hair—what was left of it—clung to her skull, and wine-colored stains swept across the skin below her eyes.

She's dead. The fear that clenched Anna's heart nearly dropped her to her knees. Then, as she tiptoed closer to the bed, she realized that the hissing, pumping, dripping machines were keeping her mother alive. Anna reached out to touch her mother's arm and found it surprisingly warm while her own hand was cold, clammy, and shaky. Again, she nearly collapsed to the floor, but a hard, metal-framed chair caught her fall. Anna heard a strange sound like the whoosh of air from a person who has been punched in the gut. She looked around the room in fear and confusion. Wasn't she the only one besides her mother in this quiet, lonely room?

Then Anna realized that the sound had come from her. Hot tears spilled onto her face. *Mother could very well die in the hours or days ahead,* she thought. This once vital, bossy, opinionated, generous, raven-haired woman who had dominated her world for the past seventeen years might not survive this time.

She didn't know how much time passed as she sat on the hard chair trying to warm her cold, cold hand on her mother's warm yet wasted arm. She prayed silently to the Jesus of her favorite childhood hymn. *If it's true that Jesus loves me,* she thought, *where is He now? Where is the all-powerful Father when she—and her mother—needed Him the most?*

Somehow Anna made it to her feet, whispered goodbye to the seemingly lifeless specter that was her mother, and stumbled out of the room. She had never opened her eyes or responded to Anna's touch. Had she known that Anna was there? Whether she had or not, Anna saw her and—perhaps for the first time since January's radical mastectomy—knew that she was dying, despite the surgeries, the drugs, and all the prayers sent to a God who had turned a deaf ear.

Anna walked blindly past the nurses' station where the busy staff didn't notice the ashen-faced girl walk by clutching her bag of sandy beach provisions. She found herself in a small waiting area and threw herself down on the brown Naugahyde couch, and began to cry again.

"If You loved her," she wept aloud, "if You loved me, You wouldn't let this happen! She doesn't deserve this! It's not fair!

"If she dies, who will take care of Robbie and me? Dad doesn't care about us anymore. Where will we live? Where will we go?"

Deep inside, Anna knew that it wasn't fair, yet alone and unprepared, she couldn't make sense of it—her first full-frontal view of the dreadfully unjust nature of life. Worse, no one was there to help her understand. Eventually, the tears stopped, and Anna took the elevator to the lobby where she found a phone booth. She dug around in the bottom of her bag and found a dime among a handful of change and dialed the number before she remembered that Karen wasn't at the house.

"Hey, Anna!" Robbie ran ahead of Karen and grabbed Anna's arm. Karen looked at her niece's face and stopped midstride. "What's happened? How's Audrey?"

"I think you'd better go see her," Anna said quietly. "Robbie and I will wait here."

When Karen finally reappeared, her face was as drawn and pale as Anna's. The two exchanged a sad, worried look over Robbie's head before they walked out into the glaring sun.

Anna was silent on the drive to her aunt and uncle's house. She wanted to go home. She wanted to see David, the boy who had been a constant friend and, more recently, her young lover. She wanted to feel the quiet strength of Puget Sound and the towering evergreens that shaded her backyard. She wanted to feel the mist on her face and smell the earthy aroma of the forest she loved to walk through when everything else failed to heal the wounds of the day.

Robbie leaned forward from his place in the back seat and touched Anna's shoulder. "How is she? You look so sad. What's going on?"

"I don't really know, Robbie. She looked pretty bad, but I'm sure she'll be better tomorrow when the anesthesia wears off."

"We'll try to get permission for you to see her tomorrow, Robbie," Karen said. "In the meantime, let's try not to worry too much. Hank will be home soon. Let's just get home and get some dinner started."

Anna glanced at Robbie in the back; he had settled down into the seat and seemed to be appeased, at least for the moment.

When Karen pulled into the garage, Anna wanted nothing more than to close herself off in the bedroom she shared with her little brother and write some letters to David and her friend Valerie. Maybe by pouring her heart out to them she could ease the ache in her heart and mind. However, before she could make it to the bedroom, her aunt asked for her help in the kitchen. The air between them was negatively charged as Anna helped put away the groceries and then turned toward her room, but Karen grabbed her arm and pulled her back around. "Where are you going now?"

Since her mother's relapse, Karen had been moody and sometimes downright hostile toward Anna, although Anna had complied with every demand for kitchen help, every call for cleaning bathrooms and vacuuming floors, and more. Now, her anger toward her aunt surprised her, but she couldn't contain it any longer.

"I'm tired." Anna sighed. "I just want to go lay down."

"Well, wouldn't that be nice," Karen said with a sneer that stunned Anna. "But I still have dinner to make and Robbie to take care of. And calls to make to your sisters and your mother's doctor. I can't believe how selfish you are, Anna!"

"What? Why are you so mad at me?" Anna pushed her tangled hair behind her ears and looked directly at her aunt. "And why weren't you with me this afternoon instead of doing whatever it was you were doing with Robbie? He's not a baby. He could have stayed here by himself, and I could have used some support this afternoon!"

Her lips began to tremble. "Have you ever thought about that?"

Karen stopped in her tracks, obviously taken aback by Anna's vehement response. But then, Karen's tough exterior seemed to soften just enough to give Anna the courage to talk about her terrible visit with her mother. Tears followed, washing her young, sun-kissed face with grief and fear. Karen finally stepped forward to hold her niece and then guided her to the couch, fishing in the pocket of her apron for a tissue to wipe her face.

"I had no idea that Audrey would be in such terrible shape," Karen said. "You're right, I could have left Robbie here. You shouldn't have been there alone. I'm sorry, Anna."

Anna lifted her head and turned her blue eyes—still brimming with tears—to Karen's, so like her own. "I just don't understand why you've been so mean to me lately. I've been trying really hard to help out, but you're never happy with me or anything I do. What have I done that's so terrible?"

Karen turned her body slightly away from Anna and fumbled for a cigarette in a box on the table in front of them, lit it, and then inhaled deeply before she spoke.

"I've been scared to death." She picked at the soggy tissue she still held in her hands and flicked the ash from her cigarette into the ashtray in front of her. "Your mother is not just my sister, Anna, she's my best friend. Even though we live far apart, we've always been so close . . . I just don't know what I'd do, or be, without her."

So that's it. Anna looked at Karen and, for the first time, could see the depth of her sadness. She leaned toward her aunt, collapsing into her arms, and their silent tears filled the room with a vast despair. Still, Anna felt more comforted and safe than she had in weeks.

Finally, Karen spoke softly into Anna's sun-bleached hair, looking out the patio doors at the vibrant red bougainvillea she'd planted there a month before. "I'm sorry, Anna. I really am. Hank's been telling me to lighten up with you."

Just then, Robbie barged in through the front door with all his boyish energy. Karen and Anna quickly wiped their faces, slid away from each other, and turned toward the boy whose innocence was like a breath of cool morning air in June.

"Hey, you." Karen stubbed out her cigarette and got up to return to the kitchen. "How about helping me mix up some meat loaf?"

By the time Anna's mother died early that December, she knew more about caring for the terminally ill than many registered nurses. She knew that along with the drugs came chills and high temps, nausea and fatigue, and occasional bursts of energy when the need to do something like sew a woolen dress or knit a pair of baby booties could not be denied. Anna knew how to give an expert bed bath and administer morphine when physical and emotional pain became too much to bear. And she knew that talking about it would never really assuage the heartbreak she felt as she went on about her life.

Karen and Hank never showed up for the memorial or the burial; her aunt said she needed to mourn her sister alone. Besides, Virginia—the "bad" sister, in Karen's opinion—had swooped in at the end to help out, attempting to negate years of estrangement and neglect. Maybe that was why Karen hadn't come. But Anna also knew that judgment was not hers; she had learned that as well.

"I hear you're off to Washington State next year, Anna," one of her mother's friends said to her after the memorial.

"Yes," she said, "and Robbie and I will be in Oregon with Virginia's family this summer. Maybe we'll be able to recover a little from the past year."

As she said it, Anna felt once again the warmth of that Southern

California beach, the screeching gulls, and the childish screams of joy along the strand. In her mind she drank deeply of the shimmery light and salty air; maybe, just maybe, it would be enough to sustain her during the unimaginable years to come.

Leslie Heineman

Leslie Heineman has a journalism degree from the University of Colorado at Boulder and works as a freelance writer and editor from her home office in Anacortes, Washington. She has written a memoir titled No Longer Ordinary and has just begun to dabble in fiction and short story.

DRIVING WITH LADY CHATTERLEY

By

Linda Stewart Henley

We probably should have planned a less ambitious trip. But we were going to visit family in England and Scotland, and the various members lived in different areas, from south to north, some in remote places, and we needed a car.

My husband Vince was driving and assigned to me the role of navigator. Vince was a superb map reader and had ordered detailed maps of the entire country before our trip. I had the maps in a pile on the floor beside me when we left the car rental lot. Not surprisingly, he wanted me to tell him the directions by following the maps. But doing this was challenging. First I had to choose the right map and orient myself to our location. Then there were many roundabouts, and calling out the exit before the signs whizzed past meant that we missed most of them the first time around. The roundabouts assume that you know the next town in the direction you are heading, and there were so many crowded on the map that I got dizzy just looking. We kept circling, meanwhile trying to dodge the cars and lorries that, unlike us, knew where they were going. I wasn't much help. Vince was not impressed. In self defense, I told him the Brits had taken down the road signs in the late 1930s to confuse the Germans in case they invaded the country during World War II and had never replaced them.

We had initially balked at paying for it, but finally decided to try using the GPS navigation system. I switched it on. You had to enter the postal code to indicate your destination, and that involved a search through the travel documents because the information wasn't on our maps. Finally I found the code. The voice of a well-bred English lady informed us she was locating our position. Then she told us, "From the roundabout, take the third exit." We missed it and went around again, and were instructed, more urgently, to take the third exit. From then on, we listened to the snooty lady as she guided us in and out of the labyrinth of roads and roundabouts to the south coast. We didn't really like her, but we agreed that she took some of the stress out of the trip. She did not seem to be aware of changes in road conditions, such as detours and one-way streets, and if we ignored her instructions and failed to make a turn, she would get sulky. There would be a silence after we had consistently disobeyed, followed by the command, "At the first opportunity, make a u-turn."

We were faced with a dilemma: we could ignore the lady, who I dubbed Lady Chatterley, or I could start reading the maps again. We decided to give her a chance, though I resisted obeying the electronic voice whose presence invaded our vacation. She was opinionated. I hated her arrogance. I felt inadequate, that my diction needed attention. The voice would come on without warning, without any regard for us or a conversation that she might be interrupting. To make things worse, Vince started to like her and didn't seem to mind being guided by her frosty, but polite, instructions. I found myself becoming jealous and told Vince she wasn't really as smart as she sounded.

One day, she proved me right. She calmly directed us through a series of narrow lanes that dead-ended at a residential garage. There was scarcely any room to turn around, and the house next to it was nowhere near the hotel in Romsey where we wanted to go. The snooty voice kept telling us, "You have reached your destination." I finally had my opportunity to put her in her place. "You see, Lady Chatterley is not omniscient," I smugly remarked, "this garage is *certainly not* our destination," and pressed the button to silence her.

From then on, we used her only when we really needed to. After three weeks, she had driven us both slightly mad. One day Vince said, looking at me out of the corner of his eye, "I wonder what perfume she uses."

"Probably essence of gasoline," I shot back.

But we did reach most places with her help. Our travels took us from London south to the county of Hampshire, then north through the Cotswolds, and finally to Edinburgh in Scotland before returning to London. By U.S. standards, this is not much driving, distance-wise, fewer than a thousand miles. But the roads are crowded, and on the motorway north we encountered torrential rainstorms. We could hardly see for the water cascading onto the windshield thrown up from lorry tires ahead of us. The roads flooded, and the public warning system repeatedly over-rode the Lady's refined speech with a rough admonition to take an alternative route because of flooding. In this case, we found that by referring to the map we could find alternate roads better than by listening to the instructions that the authorities barked at us.

On the last day of our trip, we thought we would use the Lady to steer us to the car rental return. However, we didn't know the postal code for the destination. So I once again assumed the role of navigator. My only objective was to look out for the car rental return sign and warn Vince in enough time for him to change lanes for the exit. We kept to the middle lane of the five-lane motorway as we approached Heathrow airport. I strained to read all the signs ahead of us. We thought we had allowed plenty of leeway to arrive before our flight boarded, but we realized that we were already running out of time. Suddenly I saw the sign: Car Hire Returns Next Left Exit.

"Turn left!" I screamed. Too late. We passed the exit and seemed to be heading into the airport arrivals ramp. "We need to turn around," I said, stating the obvious. Without any more prompting, Vince switched lanes and exited at the first opportunity.

We found ourselves in the parking garage. There was no way to back out, and we were beside the ticket machine with its white entry pole.

"We will have to take a ticket to get in," Vince said, "and then pay to get out." Vince is a careful driver, but he spun a wheel to get to the first pay machine we could find. We stopped, and I got out, fumbling in my purse for change. "Do you have any pounds?" I asked, "We need two to get out of here."

We only just made it to the car rental garage and to the check-in counter at the airport before the cutoff. It had not been the relaxing vacation we expected. But I can be generous now about Lady Chatterley, and readily admit that she was the better navigator.

LINDA STEWART HENLEY

Linda Stewart Henley has written poetry for many years and has recently started writing fiction. She enjoys all the arts, especially painting. She is happy to have her story included in the Anthology and hopes that readers can relate to the story. She is a self-avowed dinosaur and is usually unsympathetic to technology. She was born in England and has lived in the United States since she was sixteen, now residing in Anacortes.

Plausible Deniability

By

Vincent E. Henley

I just had come from the briefing room where the bad news, and the next assignment, had been given to me. There was evidence from multiple sources that one of our assets, specifically, one of mine, had turned into a liability. It seems that this person had decided to serve two paymasters instead of one, and that was severely frowned upon in our business. Since he was my asset, it fell to me to resolve the matter and end the liability. That was tomorrow's problem. There was still time to enjoy the day, and I walked down the long cool corridor toward the club. I heard her high heels clicking on the tile floor before I saw her.

"Mike, wait a bit," I heard a call from behind me.

It was Susan Meyer, the station chief's assistant, and a competent analyst in her own right. I turned and waited for her to catch up. Susan was one of those women who raised the blood pressure of every normal male who saw her, but she never encouraged any personal intimacy. Gently curved in all the right places, she had long, straight black hair down to mid-back, pale skin and eyes as green as emeralds. Married, and working at it, to one of the communications techs, she had never been tainted by any of the common gossip or rumors of impropriety that tended to pool around people working in closed communities. In the words of the novelist Barbara Pym, Susan was one of those "excellent women." Her Ivy League education and facility with Middle Eastern languages made her perfect for her current position. She came close and stopped; a drift of perfume filled the space between us.

"Bill wanted me to try and catch you in the briefing, but I was on the phone when the meeting ended. Roger is back. He said he wanted to talk to you, and that he'd be in the club all afternoon. He's tasked with going to Pakistan, and dealing with the other end of your liability, so in some sense you will both be working the same problem."

"Did Roger say what he wanted? How did he seem to you?" I asked.

Susan defocused her eyes, and appeared to think for a few moments. I knew she had an eidetic memory, and could give me complete details of anything she had ever seen.

"He didn't say what he wanted with you. Maybe it's just to have a drink or two. He seems different in some way, but I'm not sure why. He's a bit more introspective, thoughtful and less spontaneous than before. He took more care before speaking, almost guarded. I can't be more specific, but something about him has changed. He just isn't the same old Roger," she said.

"Has anything happened that you know of?" I asked her.

"Not that I've heard about. His network is doing well, and I think he's due some leave fairly soon. However, Bill is concerned, and he would like you to evaluate whether Roger is in a suitable mental state for this task in Pakistan before you both leave tomorrow."

"Bill wants me to evaluate a colleague, especially one as experienced as Roger? Are you certain about that?" I asked.

"Yes. Bill was very explicit about this. He doesn't want you to do an interrogation or anything like that, but he wants you to observe, listen to Roger and form an opinion. You know Roger really well. In fact, you know him better than anyone else on this station does. Bill wants your gut feel about this," she replied quietly.

"Okay, I'll do it. I'll give Bill my opinion either later today or first thing in the morning. I don't think either of us is leaving until tomorrow afternoon, so there is a window to abort if we need it. I'll go find him in the club. Thanks, Susan; please tell Bill that I understand what he wants."

Bill Loomis was the station chief, and he had been in the briefing with me just a short time before. I wondered why he hadn't delivered the message himself, unless Susan knew more about this than he did, which seemed unlikely. Perhaps he just thought I'd pay more attention and listen more carefully to Susan. He could have been right about that. She turned and walked away, back toward the station chief's office area. Susan looked as good going away as she did coming, and I enjoyed the view for a few moments as her heels tapped down the corridor. The exit from the building to the embassy club and swimming pool area was in the opposite direction, and I quickly walked toward it.

This was the late 1970s, and the "Great Game" was still being played on the Indian subcontinent, but the players had changed a bit. Once the exclusive realm of the Russians and the British, the mix had now been enriched by the addition of the Chinese, the Americans, the Iranians and several others. One was rarely certain that all the players in any hand were known and even worse, that the players knew their real masters. Little has changed in the nearly forty years since then.

I found Roger at a table on the patio next to the pool, where he already had a drink before him. It was late spring, and the monsoon had not yet arrived. The smoke from dung fueled cooking fires hung like a fog over all New Delhi, permeating the humid air with a yellowish pall and a musty fragrance. The only blue I could see was the bottom paint in the swimming pool that dominated the view. A few employees and the odd family member gathered and splashed about in the water to obtain relief from the heat. Some, like Roger, nursed drinks at tables shaded by large square umbrellas. When the weather warmed, New Delhi's power grid tended to fail, and that seemed likely this afternoon. The embassy's diesel generators had been running to keep the compound operating, lending the steady thrum of their exhaust to an otherwise quiet area. The embassy buildings shielded us from the steady noise of traffic and humanity on Panchsheel Marg, the road that ran along the northern edge of the compound.

"Mike, come on over and grab a chair. Have a drink," Roger called. I joined him at the table and he waved a waiter over. "Get the man a gin and tonic and another for me," he ordered. Roger knew my preferences as well as I did, and my best alternates when the preferences weren't available. We were old colleagues, and bumped into one another relatively frequently.

The drinks came; we toasted our health, and exchanged a few pleasantries about nothing in particular and everything in general. We were not going to discuss shop in the club area, as it wasn't a secure environment. I tried to sense whether there was anything different about the man I knew well.

I looked across the table and saw over six feet of solid, heavy-limbed muscle, where a thick neck supported a ruddy face topped by sandy hair cropped short. Rather large rectangular glasses protected eyes of flat grey-blue. I knew the lenses to be plain polycarbonate rated to stop most sidearm bullets. Light hair thickly covered his bare arms down to the base of his fingers, and he gave the impression of being a quite clumsy man. I knew that impression to be very wrong. His business card read "Management Consultant" with a firm in Geneva. While I knew the firm existed, I also knew the sort of management consulting Roger did had nothing to do with commercial business, even though he had a graduate degree in that field from Stanford. Roger cleaned up inconvenient "messes" in the far corners of the world, and that usually involved one or more people departing this plane of existence. He tended to wear florid Hawaiian shirts, and his overall appearance and manner were a bit loud and flamboyant, but that was deceptive.

I, in contrast, was slightly built, quiet and unremarkable; a gray man in a gray business. No one would have given me a second glance or remember they had seen me, and this was precisely the impression, or lack of one, I wanted to cultivate. My business card title was "Technical Consultant," and the address was a specialty electronics firm located in Amsterdam. We both worked at supplying that very precious diplomatic commodity, "plausible deniability."

"Mike, what do you think you know about life after death? How can anyone know anything about it?" Roger asked, taking me quite by surprise. This was not a question one would have associated with Roger, who was not known to be philosophical about such matters. Without giving me a chance to respond, he continued.

"Death is the most final damn thing I've ever seen," he said, as he clanked the ice in his glass and rattled the heavy gold links of his bracelet against the tabletop. "I've never seen evidence that would encourage me to believe there was anything to be experienced after death."

We began to discuss the subject, while I wondered what prompted it, and where it was going. This was so unlike Roger. We explored the question of whether there was any evidence for anything we could know about what happened after death. I held that we could not know, but that the belief of an afterlife was so universally ingrained in the human spirit that one should hold open the possibility of it existing. Roger argued the contrary position, using his personal contacts with death as evidence that there was nothing after life had departed. Perhaps he needed to believe that was the case, for clearly, something related to the question was bothering him.

The debate occupied several more gin and tonics for both of us on that sultry afternoon before the monsoon long ago, and we came to no conclusion. In the end, we agreed to disagree. Roger became more pensive, and his logic more convoluted as we talked. When the shadows lengthened across New Delhi and the air cooled a bit, Roger and I decided to dine together at one of the restaurants we enjoyed, but we set aside the discussion of an afterlife. Our work involved traveling the next day, but we saw no reason to dine only on liquid fuel. After we parted for the evening, I called Bill Loomis and told him that in my opinion Roger was perfectly fit, mentally and physically, for the task in Pakistan. I heard or observed nothing that set off alarm bells in my gut, despite the discussion of a potential afterlife. I would have trusted Roger with my life.

*****

A week later, the monsoon had still not arrived, and the thick air was oppressive with smoke. The blue paint at the bottom of the pool and the thrum of the diesel generators still dominated the scene at the club in the Embassy compound. Today, even more people splashed in the pool as everyone waited for the rains to begin washing everything clean, or at least as clean as things got in New Delhi. I found Roger at the same table we used the previous week.

Since then, Roger had journeyed to Islamabad in Pakistan where, I sensed, his task had not gone well. I had met my asset in the unlikely place of Fatehpur Sikri, an abandoned city of red stone, twenty-some miles west of Agra. A small caliber double-tap through the forehead had eliminated any future liability from my former asset, and an abandoned dry well solved the disposal problem nicely. It was unlikely that anything would be found before everyone was beyond caring that he had ever existed. After all, this was India. The ancient ghosts of Fatehpur Sikri had been increased by one.

Roger was well into his third gin and tonic when I took a chair across from him and ordered my own drink. I preferred gin gimlets, but the club never seemed to have the needed main ingredient, Rose's Lime Juice, so I ordered that universal vaccine dating from the British Raj: quinine-laced tonic water liberally diluted with gin.

Roger looked a bit worse for wear, but I couldn't tell if that was the effect of the gin or the result of his business trip. He'd been in country longer than I'd been this time around, and was probably overdue leave. I knew from Susan Meyer that he was going to be cycled back to Geneva for a while as a "Management Consultant," just as his business card indicated, but I didn't think he was going on leave.

"Well?" was all he asked.

"The meet was successful," I replied. "And you?"

He just shook his head.

"Mike, I had to do it," he said. "There was no other option. Now, I find myself wishing that your side of the argument about an afterlife is true." He took another gulp of his drink but offered little more while I tried to digest the meaning of what he said. Roger was being uncharacteristically quiet and introspective instead of his usual flamboyant self. I wasn't quite sure what to make of this change. Susan was right; something was different.

I could tell that he wanted to drink gin and not talk about Islamabad, or at least not much, and we couldn't discuss much in the club. Something about Islamabad must have been disappointing, or very difficult. Perhaps it was both. Whatever it was, Roger had changed and I could see it. That's not necessarily an asset in our business. The last thing we need is an active conscience or a significant change in behavior. I knew better than to probe too deeply, but something, as Roger saw it, had not gone well.

We sipped our gin together that afternoon, ignoring the strengthening smoke from the dung fires that ramped up toward the evening mealtime. At first, we conversed in small inconsequential phrases about nothing memorable. Roger drank at least two more gins and so did I, but he was ahead of me by several. As the afternoon wound down, and more gin flowed, Roger began to tell me in whispers more about what had happened in Islamabad. He chose his words carefully, clearly trying to tell me something without actually telling me anything. All of us had practiced this skill to perfection, including decoding the obfuscation. I was beyond being shocked at this stage of my life, but it was clear that things had been very messy for Roger in the past week, and it affected him greatly. I wondered if Roger could continue to do his work, as this incident clearly stressed him more than I'd ever seen. He wasn't quite yet a broken tool, but was near the breaking point. Bill should know about this if he didn't already.

Roger's plane wasn't leaving New Delhi until the basement hours of the morning. He wasn't driving himself to the airport, so neither of us was worried about navigating a vehicle and we kept drinking and talking. Later, we shared a light supper, and then he went to gather his sparse baggage for the trip to Geneva. I wasn't leaving for Amsterdam until two days later, so I just went to sleep off the gin.

The next morning, I went to the station chief's area, and found Susan at her desk analyzing some Farsi intercepts. She gave me a bright smile that lit up her whole face as I walked in, but I knew that was about the limit of her interaction with single men.

"What's new with the world?" I asked her.

She shrugged and turned her palms up.

"I think Iran is about to descend into the cauldron of Hell and the DCI can't get the Peanut Farmer to listen, but that's just my opinion."

"Yeah, the Shah is losing control and some of our so-called friendly countries are fanning the flames. You know about those black-robed clerics, don't you?" I asked.

"Yes, indeed," she indicated the piles of intercepts on her desk and grimaced.

"Is Bill available right now?" I asked.

"Yes. He told me earlier that he thought you would show up this morning to talk about Roger. I take it that Roger left this morning as scheduled," she replied.

"Yes, he's gone. It's about twelve hours including ground stops, so he should get back to Geneva via Frankfurt by this afternoon."

"Bill told me to send you right in, so just go ahead," she indicated the door to Bill's office.

I reluctantly turned my attention away from her, and to the obligatory chore. I entered Bill's office, and met with him briefly to give him my new opinion about Roger. I tried to discover more about what had happened in Islamabad, but all Bill would say is that the effect had been greater than planned. That could mean nearly anything, but it was really a signal that I didn't have a "need to know." I suppose I could have argued the point, but I knew from experience that I was unlikely to succeed.

I heard more about the operation in Islamabad from the internal rumor mill and it was deemed a success, if a bit excessive. Roger was blamed for collateral damage involving two small children and a woman who would have been witnesses. Roger was good at his job, but none of us can control all circumstances, and sometimes the decisions that need to be made quickly are not nice ones and have tragic outcomes. It is possible that I could have spared Roger the Islamabad assignment by giving a different opinion to Bill Loomis, but I think not. Given the same information, I would have come to the same conclusion, and therefore perhaps I share responsibility for the collateral damage.

I never saw Roger again.

Vincent E. Henley

Vince Henley is a retired computer scientist who wrote non-fiction technical prose for most of his career. In recent years, his interests have turned to fiction, and his writing now includes mystery and thriller short stories and novels, some science fiction and fantasy, and the occasional children's story. His children's tales explore the fears and angst we experienced as children but have forgotten as adults, and those things in the dark that children can see easily, but adult eyes cannot.

Life and Death
Chapter One

By

Florence House

Week One. September, El Marino, California.

Handsome Harold Hemet stiff-marched through the halls of El Marino Medical Center and plowed through the automatic doors into pea soup ground fog. "Fucking Crap!"

A document fluttered in his fist as he aimed toward the Doctor's parking lot. "No way. No. Freaking. Way." He wadded the document into a tight ball, slammed it onto an over-filled trashcan, and kicked it. Take-out cartons and paper cups escaped over the side.

Need for escape pushed stride to lope. Where was she? Ah there, there she waited, sleek and silver, haloed in the milky glow of a lone streetlight. Lope turned to sprint. He frowned at the outline of a pickup parked across two slots at the edge of light and dark. Slot hog.

Woe overtook ire. By the time he reached her, his chest heaved and tears flowed. He stroked her hood, and let the facts sink in. Lawyers were circling. He'd been kicked out of Surgery. His malpractice was canceled. El Marino had been his last chance, and he blew it.

So he made a mistake. Accidents happen. Every surgery had risks. He'd warned the woman about the risks. Damn her, she signed the consent. She was just too fat.

The apology to her husband was the best he'd ever given. God, he was sorry, so truly sorry. But what could he do? Bring her back? The asshole never looked at him, he just kept crying.

Well, hell, just get in, hit the freeway, and blow it off.

Opening the door, he put a leg in and lowered a haunch to the leather seat. As he pulled in the other leg, his keys slipped to the pavement. "Damned butter fingers." Leaning over, Harry reached down and patted the asphalt pavement.

Keys jangling, he rose victorious and stilled. Lights blinded. An engine roared. Rubber burned. "Too fast," Harry screamed, "you're coming too fast! What the fuck! Stop!"

Harry stopped. The truck stopped. The street light bowed. The light blinked out.

The weapon reversed, and idled. A flash bloomed, and died in the dark. Gears shifted as the truck rumbled away, leaving a colorful tableau for the day shift.

Sissy's Day at the Water Slides

By

Cindy Jacobson

"Those noisy things, I have to go see them," Sissy hissed.

"Oh, they sound scary," hissed Rufus.

"I've been watching them since I was born. That's been at least two months! I must see what is going on," hissed Sissy.

"Oh, you can't, Mommy and Daddy told us we had to stay away from people," Rufus hissed.

"I'm old enough to be careful." Sissy slithered over the rocks towards the loud people.

Kids and adults were splashing in all kinds of different water slides. They didn't notice a three-foot long bull snake curled up outside the fence watching them.

Sissy wanted to get a better look at what the people were doing. She slipped through the hole in the fence. Everywhere she looked, there were people.

Sissy slithered over to a slide, slipping past the people in line and onto the slide. With a flick of her tail down the slide Sissy went. The water felt cool on her skin.

"A snake, a snake, aaah!"

"I think it's a rattlesnake; run for your life!"

"Where's the rattlesnake?" Sissy hissed. She wanted out of the water and away from the rattlesnake. "Mommy, Daddy, help, help!"

"Swimmers stand back. Do not fear. Micah is here!" The young animal control man walked up to the pool of water with his net.

Micah had lived in Seattle, where the biggest snake was a foot-long garter snake. Sweating and shaking, Micah swung the net at Sissy.

Sissy landed on top of the net. As Micah continued to wave the net, Sissy went flying. Micah was screaming, people were shouting, and then Albert showed up. Albert was the local chief of police.

Sissy was so scared she wanted to go home.

"Micah, come over and watch, please," Albert said. Very carefully,

Albert took a hook and caught Sissy. Into a large wooden box, he dropped her. He quickly closed and latched the lid.

Micah and the crowd cheered.

Sissy was shaking. What was going to happen to her now, she thought? Would she ever see her family and friends again?

"Micah, help me carry the box to the truck," Albert said. Even with the snake in the box, Micah was afraid to grab the handle. "Micah, it's ok, the snake can't get you," Albert said.

Albert knew about snakes. He knew by the bull snake's size that it was only about three months old. He also knew that they live in the hills above the Clear Water Slides Park. With Sissy in her box in the back of the truck, Albert drove her and Micah up the hill to take the snake home.

With the box on its side, Albert opened the lid and pulled Sissy out with his hook. Walking away from his truck, he dropped Sissy under some bushes. Albert and Micah went back to the truck.

Sissy immediately knew where she was: three large rock piles and two sage bushes from her den. Quickly Sissy slithered home.

For now, Sissy was going to stay away from people, like her mom and dad had told her.

CALLIE

By Megan Jones

Only one way out, Callie realized, and tucked her two traveling companions, Tawa and Pinto Pony, into her carry bag.

"Sshhh." She cupped her hand over Tawa's inquisitive and squirming head. "We're outta here."

Callie held the bag tight against her body and gauged the timing of the cosmic flashes blizzarding through a black and purple sky. Now. She jumped on a lightning bolt, hung on tight and hoped for the best. The gods only knew where they'd wind up, but anywhere was better than this desolate dump of a planet, patched with quicksand and quarks, inhabited by malevolent spirits and rabid robots.

An eternal split second later she landed with a rough bounce as the bolt grounded out. The carry bag began to wiggle, squirm and punch. The cats were annoyed; an eternal split second was an eternity too long to be bagged up. She let them out and looked around. Comin' close to dusk, wherever they were. Nowhere she recognized. A line of trees with multicolored leaves ran along one edge of the field she'd landed in. Sounded like a river running and splashing just beyond them. Where did the cats get to? She whistled sharply and moments later they appeared, their coats laced with pink and yellow.

"Been playin' in the leaves, eh?" She bent to scratch a couple of arched backs. "Stay close, guys, until I figure out where we are and where we're going."

Standing erect, Callie scanned her surroundings more carefully. Grass crop of some kind growing in the field. Two hundred strides, she reckoned, to the stone fence that bordered the far edge. Another field of something beyond that and then what looked like wild country all the way to the pale purple hills rising toward the darkening sky. So. Definitely inhabited, and maybe a few dwellings nestled in the wild but, judging by the skyline, no city anywhere close. And unless this was a particularly advanced--and wealthy--planet, she'd need a city.

She turned slowly, her eyes following the march of trees that edged the field and ended at a small embankment. Through the interlaced branches of pink and yellow she spotted a bridge. Probably spanned the river she heard, and probably meant a road.

Callie knelt in the grass and spoke to her cats. "Hop up." They leapt to her shoulders, claws gripping her leather jerkin. She moved carefully through the field and, reaching the edge, scrambled up an embankment. Sure enough, there was a road. Hard surfaced in some sort of muddy-yellow material. Standing on the shoulder, she looked both ways. It stretched long to her right, more fields on either side and what looked like a row of low buildings toward the end. To her left, across the bridge, the road disappeared into trees. Which way?

Closing her eyes, she took a long, slow breath and emptied her mind, let her senses stretch. A light breeze rustled through the trees, kissed her skin and a dusky, sun toasted aroma filled her nostrils. She turned left.

Reaching the middle of the bridge, Callie stopped, leaned over the rail and watched the river flowing toward the horizon. Pinto and Tawa sprang from her shoulder to the rail, playing leapcat along its length.

"Stay close." She smiled as Pinto Pony, in mid leap, swished his bushy silken tail in acknowledgment. The cats' easy play confirmed her sense that there was no threat in the immediate vicinity. Maybe she could stay put for a day or two. That'd be good. It had been a tricky few months and some down time was definitely in order.

She turned her attention to the world in front of her and her gaze stretched out over land that rolled gently to blue hills on the horizon. It was dotted and clumped with trees and patched with neatly tended fields of head high crops. Four sturdy animals grazed at the far end of a grassy pasture just below the bridge, and beyond them a long, yellow roof peaked above a grove of pink trees. A blue sun was over half way down the far side of a darkening green sky. Maybe an hour of light left, depending on the sun cycle.

Whistling the cats to her, Callie entered the trees and saw that the road curved in and out of sight, along the base of a low, forested hill. How far to someplace where she could get some real food and a bed for the night? She shook her head, put her mind in loose, and kept moving. The cats wandered, nosed around bushes and brambles, hopped in and out of a roadside ditch, but still kept pace with her long-legged stride.

The tree-canopied road wound and twisted, led her around three or four long, gentle curves, looped around a small, simple dwelling set next to a shed, and at last opened out of the trees into a village. To her left, she saw what had to be a playground. She recognized swings, a slide and jungle bars. The building at the back of the playground, nestled against the hill she'd just rounded, would be a school. Pretty much like on Vivala. So there were humans here. Good. Made things simpler.

Callie looked for the cats and saw they'd gone ahead of her. Pinto Pony strutted like a proud young prince down a footpath running parallel to the road and fronting a row of six or seven small buildings. Tawa pranced lightly beside him, ears on forward alert. Shrugging, Callie followed their lead.

She passed what looked like an indoor market, several humans and a Kalindian moving about inside. Interesting. Not a lot of Kalindians traipsing around the galaxy. She paused, scanning her environment for more detail. Several figures walked along the road toward a breeze-rippled lake, deep magenta in the fading light. Two tall ones were probably Axliads, but the other two looked full human. Better and better. Probably a human settled planet, but not unused to Others. More things got simpler.

Two doors down, the cats had stopped. A perky melody skipped and hopscotched into the spring evening as a woman and two men stepped out onto the footpath, laughing and calling to someone behind them. A pub. There'd be food. Callie's stomach growled. She noted the bright red liquid gel sign above the door. The Wild Card. Another good sign.

"Stay close." She bent to scratch behind inquisitive ears. "There'll be some chow when I get back."

She entered the pub, a long narrow room that widened out at the end of the bar on her left. Several tables were occupied, and four people sat at the bar, but it was a light crowd. The musos, on a raised platform at the back, finished the tune they were playing and announced a break. Moving to the bar, Callie fished for her money pouch.

"Any Abbey Ale?" she asked as the bartender approached.

"On tap," the young woman replied. "Short or tall?"

"Very tall, please," Callie said. "How much?"

"Four creds." The barmaid filled a tall glass with rich amber liquid.

"Callie?" Surprise and disbelief colored the voice.

She spun quickly, balanced, sure and ready. Her eyes widened. So did her mouth as a gasp of recognition escaped. She stood stock still and stared. A lean and wiry man, alone at a far table, sat equally stock still and stared back. Then a great laugh propelled him from his chair. He strode across the room to grasp her by the shoulders and look intently at her face. "Callista Lydelli! What in the name of galactic ghosts are you up to and when did you get here?" He pulled her in to a tight hug.

"Jax?" Callie asked his shoulder.

"That'd be me," he answered. "Always figured you'd turn up again someday," Pushing her out arm's length, he studied her for long seconds. Then he asked, "Runnin' or roamin'?"

"Runnin'," Callie acknowledged.

"Breathin' room?"

"Think so." She nodded. Not likely anyone could trace a cosmic lightning bolt. The black mage and his goons would have to start over.

"Good. So let's hear your story." Jax slipped his arm around her shoulder and took a step toward his table.

Callie turned out of his hold, held up her money pouch. "Gotta pay for my drink."

His long fingers closed around her hand. "On my chit, Mina," he said to the bartender as he walked Callie away from the bar. "First one's on me, Trouble. Good to see you still breathin'."

Callie laughed, tossed her short purple curls. "Haven't been called that in way too long! And I am so happy to see your face!" Curiosity crinkled around her eyes. "Also surprised. You on a Circus job here? Wherever 'here' is."

"Nope," Jax answered. He sat down and gestured for Callie to do the same. "Tell y'about it later. Right now I wanta know who's after y'and why."

"A black mage. I stole the Serenity Sapphire from him." She took a sip of ale and smiled approvingly. "Good Abbey. Import or domestic?"

Jax raised an eyebrow. "Domestic," he answered. "Quit stallin'. Which mage?"

Callie frowned. "Jasper. From CatsEye."

Jax shook his head in resigned exasperation laced with grudging admiration. "I named you well," he declared, raising his glass. "How'd you get messed up with that galactic creep show?"

"Sisters of Mercy," Callie replied. "Jasper stole it from them. They called me. I answered."

"Ohh-kaay," Jax responded, dubious. "How 'bout y'start from the beginning."

"Any chance I can get some food first? Haven't eaten for a couple of days, and I'm hungry. So are Pinto Pony and Tawa."

"The cats!" Jax exclaimed. "They're still with you? Where are they?"

"Just outside. I told 'em to stay close."

"You can bring 'em inside," Jax told her. "Why don't you go get 'em and I'll order some food. They make a great spicy seafood mix-up here. Sound good?"

"Sounds yummy-delicious." Callie rose from the table. "And some fish for the cats?"

"I think that could be easily done," Jax drawled, smiling.

Callie smiled back and headed for the door. When she returned, a cat on each shoulder, Jax had come back to their table. He handed her two plump fish and the cats meowed.

"Say thanks to Jax." Callie snagged a broadsheet from the empty table next to them, spread it on the floor by her chair and dropped the fish in the middle. "Chow down, guys, but remember your manners."

The cats were already busy and didn't bother to respond.

"Mix-up is gettin' mixed up," Jax said. "Be out in a bit. Meanwhile... from the beginning." He picked up his glass and sat back.

"Right." Callie picked up her glass and took a swig of ale. "Three lunars past, the Sisters sent a call for help via dreamline. I was on Axlor at the time. Just finished winding up a gig for Solarix Galactic, so I got me and the cats to an ITM portal and hyperspaced it to Elisia. Sister Maya met me and from there it was just a short hop by skipjet to Serenity where Magda, the High Sister, told me what had happened and asked me to help get it back."

"That's a big ask," Jax protested. "Jasper's a very dangerous and high powered dude. Messin' with him could get you dead, or worse, mind twisted."

"Doesn't matter. If you remember, I was good as dead from the scratches I got from a scorpio vine when we went in with Jezz and Hanna to retrieve Gita from that prison on Babbleon."

"Not likely I'll ever forget." Jax grimaced. "By the time we got back to the Circus, your skin was poison green and you were unconscious, barely breathing. Max took one look at you, grabbed the skipjet controls and took off like a cloud of angry little brumbles were after him." Jax shook his head in slow disbelief, remembering. A sharp exhale escaped his nose and he continued the story.

"Flyin' like a mad man. Slingshots around an asteroid or two and we wind up at that stardust pocket out past Elisia which turns out to be a protective mist for this planet I'd never heard of. Max guides us through--I don't know how--and we land on the planet where two women in cloaks meet us and carry you and the cats away. Max skipped us back out into true space and on to Xylon. After that, you were just absent."

"First time I've heard that bit of the story." Callie finished her drink and regarded her old friend with affection. "Those cloaked women were Sisters from the temple and they were the ones pulled me back from the black hole I was in."

"Max said if anyone could save you, it'd be the Sisters of Mercy," Jax said. "He told us they were the best, most skilled whole-healers in the galaxy."

He leaned forward, tugged a purple curl and grinned. "Guess he was right. Here you are, in livin' color! Gotta say you look a whole lot better than the last time I saw you. That green wasn't a good look with your hair." The grin faded and an eyebrow raised. "That was six, maybe seven solturns past. Where y'been all this time, Trouble?"

"That's a long song, my friend," Callie said. "It can wait. I've got the Sapphire and I have to get it back to the Sisters soon. It needs to be in the temple, in their hands."

"I can prob'ly help with that." Jax covered Callie's hands with his. "I gotta couple ideas, but we can talk about 'em later. Kip at my place tonight 'n tomorrow we'll figure it out."

Callie nodded agreement. Be good to lay back with her old teammate for an evening and stop thinking about the next step for a little while.

MEGAN JONES

MEGAN JONES graduated in 1964 from Sedro Woolley High. After completing an honors BA in English, she took off for 18 months of backpacking around Europe. While working in Edinburgh, she met a Scotsman who followed her when she returned to the USA. They married and immigrated to Australia where she taught English at a Melbourne high school and then at a TAFE college. After nearly 30 years in Oz, she returned to the US and, realizing she needed something new, discovered the SVWL and decided to give writing a shot.

Role Model

By

Kathleen Kaska

Every Thursday evening Katy treated herself to a triple dose of glamour. At six-thirty Ginger sauntered onto the screen in her sequined gown causing the Skipper, the Professor, and any male who happened to be marooned on Gilligan's Island that week, to drool. Then Mrs. Emma Peel of the *Avengers* volleyed with her counterpart Mr. Steed. Mrs. Peel always remained cool in the face of danger. She was daring and witty, never at a loss for words. But the true inspiration occurred at eight when Morticia Adams crossed her arms, snapped her fingers, and smiled coyly at the camera—beautiful, intelligent, sensuous. Morticia was everything Katy was not. Mrs. Peel and Ginger were everything Katy was not. But it was Morticia who provided the inspiration Katy needed.

Her mother would be pissed as hell, but who cared, Katy thought. Her mother didn't have stringy blonde hair that hung limp like dead fish on a trout line. Her mother didn't have to go to PE with older girls who's bra size was greater than Katy's score on last week's algebra test. Her mother would never understand that Katy didn't have time to wait for the natural transformation into womanhood. And when it did finally occur, Katy held no illusion that she would look anything like her gorgeous heroines.

Timing was everything, and so far so good.

It was five o'clock on Monday morning, and the sky was beginning to brighten. Her family wouldn't need the bathroom for another hour. While Katy waited, she picked up the bottle and read the directions once more, just to make sure she'd gotten them right. Black Beauty, the label read, guaranteed to give hair that midnight sheen. There was a picture of a woman with wavy black hair cascading down her white shoulders. Katy had studied the different brands at Old Corner Drugstore. Black Beauty by Clairol was the most expensive, and Katy didn't have enough money. She thought about purchasing a cheaper brand, but she remembered her dad always saying, "you get what you pay for." No, it was Black Beauty or nothing. Katy was about to give up on her plan when things started to happen last Saturday morning.

Katy was still in bed with her pillow over her head. Her two youngest sisters were awake early watching cartoons with the TV blaring. Katy had no plans for the weekend, and was destined to face another disappointing week at school. Last Friday, Ben had avoided her all day, and as she was leaving school, she saw him walking shoulder to shoulder with Lynnette Luster. They were laughing—the type of laughter that told Katy her no-good boyfriend and the school slut were a bit too friendly. There was no way Katy could complete with Lynnette Luster. Lynnette was wild. Her older sister LaDonna had gotten pregnant the year before; it was only a matter of time before Lynnette followed in LaDonna's footsteps. The voluptuous Luster sisters——they even looked fertile, in a daring, damn-you sort of way. They plowed through boys like hay bailers, swooping them up where they stood, entwining them in a wad of emotions, and then dumping them in the field to rot. Katy pictured Ben lying on his back in the dirt, dried up, staring at the sky as his last breath fluttered from his lips. "Help me." Katy was striking a match to light Ben's foot when the phone rang.

Her mother had answered the upstairs extension. It was Marsha Fox wanting Katy to babysit, and Katy could hear Marsha's voice coming through the telephone line loud and clear. "Sorry about the last minute call, but Reggie Snail and his Five Slimmers were too hung over to drive back from Houston. They had to cancel this evening's gig at the Fox Hole. We were lucky to get the Vadelka Polka Band at the last minute. Whenever they play, they draw a crazy crowd. You know, all those Czech folks living around Tours are polka crazy. They flock into town like locusts after a fresh crop of corn. I need to help bar tend tonight."

Katy swore she'd never babysit for the Fox kids again. Hellions, they were. Last time it took her more than an hour to get all the catsup off the TV. The red mess slid down the screen and over the control knobs. Katy had to remove each one and clean the stems. Little Darren Fox had a fixation with squirt bottles. Marsha should have never bought that latest Tupperware wonder, those red and yellow plastic condiment bottles, perfect for picnics. One time Darren squirted mustard into the chamber of Freddy Fox's pistol, and Katy had to call the VFW Club where Marsha and Freddy were playing bingo. Freddy said not to worry, at least Darren hadn't loaded the gun with ammunition.

The Foxes paid their sitters very well—combat pay Katy called it. She could hear the wavering in her mother's voice. Katy sat up in bed. "It's okay, Mom. I'll sit for them," Katy called from her room. She'd borrow the money from her sister, Karla, buy the hair rinse, and with the money she earned sitting, she could pay Karla back right away. Karla had saved every cent she'd ever earned. She was planning a trip to Paris as soon as she graduated from high school.

Katy rose early on Monday, locked the bathroom door, and got down to business. When she unwrapped the towel from her head, she almost lost her breath. Black streams trickled from her hairline. But it worked for Carolyn Jones, and Katy was confident it would work for her. In the *Biography of Femme Fatales,* Katy read that the actress' career had finally taken off after she dyed her hair. Overnight, she was transformed from a cute blonde into a black-haired bombshell. The metamorphosis eventually led to her landing the famous role of Morticia Adams on the Adams Family. Katy didn't hope for that much luck, she only needed a little to teach Ben a lesson.

Katy combed through the tangles. Instead of using her hot rollers today, she blow-dried her hair, combing it as straight as she could. She parted it down the middle and let it hang. Her hair was not as long as Morticia's, but the effort was almost as stunning.

The smell of coffee drifted upstairs and Katy knew she had only a few minutes before her father came up to shower. She cleaned the sink, hid the stained towel in the bottom of the clothes hamper, and slipped out of the bathroom and into her room.

Karla was just waking up and she screamed when Katy walked in. "Mommmm . . ."

Katy placed her hand over her sister's mouth. "I never told Mom it was you who broke her rose candy dish." Karla got the message, and Katy removed her hand.

"You scared the shit out of me. I didn't know who was in our room. That's what you wanted the money for? Mom's gonna kill you."

"She won't find out."

"What are you gonna do, go down to breakfast wearing Dad's old motorcycle helmet?"

"You're going to tell them that I forgot I had an algebra test this morning, and I'm leaving for school early to study with Angela."

"What about after school?"

"I also bought a bottle of Rinse Away. Mom's helping decorate the church for Easter and she won't be here when I come home from school. I'll rinse it out then."

"Mom will find out anyway."

"Well, I'll worry about that later."

Katy didn't have a black dress, so she selected last year's Christmas dress. It was red velvet with fury black trim sewn around the collar and cuffs. With her fishnet hose, she actually looked dangerous.

Katy had just sat down in the library when Angela walked by. "Oh . . . my . . . god! Angela rushed over. "Your hair!"

In her entire life, Katy never remembered being so nervous. Her insides were melting and acid bubbled in her stomach.

"I can't believe it!" Angela touched Katy's black hair as if it were fairy wings. "What made you do it?"

"It was time for a change," Katy said, forcing her throat open to speak.

"Ben will drop dead," Angela giggled.

"That's the idea," Katy said, feeling like Morticia for the first time since she unwrapped her towel from her head early this morning. "Do you think I'll get his attention?"

"I'll say," Angela said.

The bell rang for first period and Katy felt rooted to the chair. Her first class was biology. They were scheduled to dissect squid. Katy mustered her courage and rushed in at the last minute. She sat down at her assigned lab table near the front of the room. Whispers echoed behind her, but she kept her head erect and waited for the teacher to arrive.

Miss Pearl Medford had taught biology at West High for at least two hundred years. She stood six feet two in flats. She had a man's haircut, a gravelly voice, and she always wore the same style shift dress. Her stout figure looked as if it would fit snugly into an elevator shaft. She had never married, and lived with her father on a chicken farm outside of town. She was rumored to be a hermaphrodite, and when she wasn't teaching biology she raised Pomeranians. She was Katy's favorite teacher.

Nothing bothered or surprised Miss Medford. In her long tenure, she had seen it all; pregnant teenagers, teenagers who had returned to school after a stint in prison, and teenagers who fainted at the sight of pig intestines spilling out of an open gut. So when Miss Medford walked in, she immediately squelched the snickers by telling Katy how nice she looked today. Three minutes later, the squid specimens were in the pans, and Katy was no longer the center of attention.

As usual, Ben was tardy. Katy imagined him and Lynnette making out behind the stage curtains in the auditorium, but she kept her attention focused on finding the squid's ink sac, a silvery bag near the small intestine. Ben slithered in, kept his head down, and sat down next to Katy. He offered to pin the mantle to the wax as Katy sliced it back.

"I can handle it," she said. "Just watch and try not to screw things up." It was the first time Katy had used the word "screw" in that context. Ben never admitted it, but Katy knew the dissection unit made him queasy.

Then Ben noticed Katy's hair. He let out a pathetic squeal and dropped his dissecting pin. It caught in Katy's fishnets. Ben tried to untangle it; but touching Katy's leg made his fingers shake. Finally, with one quick tug he dislodged the pin, ripping a hole in Katy's hose.

"Oh, Katy, I'm so sorry."

"No problem. I have several more pair." Suddenly Katy was feeling a bit macabre. She snatched the pin from Ben's hand and jabbed it in the middle of the squid's eye, shooting a stream of formaldehyde in his face.

"Katy, how about meeting me after school," Ben said, holding a paper towel over his eye. "There's a baseball game at four. Maybe we could go for a ride after the game." He softly nudged her arm.

"Can't," Katy said. "I'm busy. I'm helping Pearl sort out the squid after school, and then we're going to her farm. She's going to show me how to castrate roosters."

Ben's eyes rolled back in his head; his chair tilted backwards. He passed out cold before he hit the floor. Miss Medford looked at Katy and shrugged her shoulders. Katy just smiled.

After school, Katy did stay and help her biology teacher. Caught up in talking squid anatomy, Katy forgot about Ben, forgot about her hair, forgot about the time. About four-thirty, like a freakish Cinderella, she rushed from the lab and called home to see if the coast was clear.

Karla answered.

"Karla, I'm late. Please tell me Mom and Dad aren't home yet."

"It's okay. Mom will be back later than she thought. She called Marsha

Fox to help decorate the church. Marsha came by with Darren and the little shit ran upstairs and locked himself in the bathroom. It took them an hour to get him out, so they got a late start. Mom won't be home for a couple of hours.

"Great, I'll be there in ten minutes. Could you have everything ready for me? I still have to worry about Dad coming home."

Katy left school and headed home through the alleys. At the first trash can, she took off her shoes, shed her torn fishnets, and sprinted home. Karla met Katy at the top of the stairs.

"Thanks. I'll just get out of this stupid dress and get started."

Karla stood there—silent.

"What?! What's the matter?"

"It's gone."

"What's gone?"

"Your Rinse Away."

"What? How could it be gone? I had it all prepped and ready to go. It was in the cabinet under the sink."

"Darren Fox must have swiped it. You know how he is about squirt bottles."

"I'm dead. Dad will be home in less than an hour. I'm dead."

"Relax. I'll go to Old Corner Drugs and buy you another bottle."

"I'm broke."

"Don't worry. This one's on me."

Katy gave Karla a hug and started to cry.

Karla pushed her away. "I'll be back in fifteen minutes. Hang tight."

Katy changed into her jeans and T-shirt and went to the kitchen. She had gotten so much attention at lunch that she didn't bother to eat. Now starving, she scarfed down two peanut butter and jelly sandwiches and finished off the milk. She was washing the dishes when the phone rang. It was Karla.

"I'm sorry, Katy. The drugstore's all out of Rinse Away. You must have bought the last bottle. I called Walgreens. They have some. I won't be able to get there and be home for at least forty-five minutes."

"Hurry! Just hurry!" Katy hung up the phone just as her father drove up. It was too late. Suddenly she didn't feel like Morticia Adams. She felt like Wednesday Adams. Wednesday the child who never smiled. Wednesday who wallowed in remorse. Wednesday who slept in a coffin.

That's what Katy needed, a coffin. She could climb in and close the lid on what was about to become the worst day of her life. She walked into the living room and sank down into the sofa. She'd just take her medicine, and get it over with.

Her father walked in, looked at Katy, and paused. Then he gave her a big smile and winked. He went to the foot of the stairs and called, "Katy, get down here. There's a friend of yours waiting in the living room." Then he changed his clothes and went outside to mow the lawn.

Kathleen Kaska

Kathleen Kaska writes the award-winning Sydney Lockhart Mysteries. Her two books, Murder at the Arlington and Murder at the Luther, were Pulpwood Queens (largest book group in the country) bonus-books. She writes the Classic Mystery Triviography Series, which includes The Agatha Christie Triviography and Quiz Book, The Alfred Hitchcock Triviography and Quiz Book, and The Sherlock Holmes Triviography and Quiz Book. The Hitchcock and the Holmes books were finalists for the 2013 EPIC award in nonfiction. Her nonfiction book, The Man Who Saved the Whooping Crane: The Robert Porter Allen Story was published by University Press of Florida in 2012.

THE LOCOMOTIVE

By

Judith Kirscht

Roland "Skip" Barnaby scratched his grey whiskers and stared at the red and white FOR SALE sign with the black 'SOLD' slapped onto the front of it. The end of things. That's what it said. That's what it was.

"Get a move on." Daisy passed through the living room carrying a stack of linens. Her voice was weary, deadened by repetition. "Sittin' won't get that railing fixed."

One more chore. Always one more going nowhere. He got up with a groan and turned from the browned-out lawn beyond the window, and gazed around at the lumpy sofa, the threadbare rug, and Daisy's collection of pictures that never changed. She kept dusting it all, picture by picture, table by table, kept vacuuming the threadbare rug with the stain in one corner hidden by the crocheted footstool he kept tripping over. Like a flywheel that keeps turning long after the machine has stopped. He couldn't see the point of it.

With a sigh, Skip headed for the basement stairs, testing the banister as he went down. Wasn't that bad. Not worth fussing about that he could see, but the buyers had bitched about it so … just do it. The way he'd done everything else for who knows how many years. To fill up days that meant nothing.

He lifted a box of garden tools from the saw table and gazed at the rusty blade. He doubted he could get it running or do much with it if he did, but he dragged it from its corner, nonetheless. The leg of the saw table caught on the edge of a cardboard box and dumped it. He swore.

Bowls, vases, toy soldiers, and cannons rolled out onto the floor and stopped his breath. Had he made those? He frowned as the memory of a vanished self seeped through some crack.

"What was that racket?" Daisy called from upstairs.

"Just a box of junk," he answered. Then he picked up a piece, and his being stilled.

A wooden steam locomotive, complete with pistons that worked, a wooden engineer, and a funnel of a smokestack.

"That was for Billy." Daisy's voice came from behind his shoulder.

He didn't answer. Didn't need to. Their gazes came together on the gift never given. On the boy killed sledding on Christmas Eve.

Then the tears burst through the cracked barrier, and with them, the empty years. On and on until there was nothing left but a shell of himself with Daisy gripping his wrist.

"Here." He handed her the engine, then gathered the other polished wooden objects and put them in a fresh box. "Pack these to go." He saw that her blue eyes had lit with hope and patted her hand before turning away to polish the rust from the saw. He had stairs to fix.

Judith Kirscht

Judith Kirscht moved to Washington State to write fiction full time and has published several novel excerpts and short stories in addition to the novel and the essay that won the awards back in her student days. She shares a house overlooking Puget Sound with an old friend, four basenjis and a drawer full of yet unpublished work.

COUSIN JIMMY:
A TRUE TALE MORE OR LESS

BY

LINDA MOORE KURTH

Cousin Jimmy grew up on a farm in the lush Willamette Valley of Oregon, in the white clapboard farmhouse that his grandparents had built with their own hands. At his birth, Jimmy weighed in at about 30 pounds. Neighbors who lived two miles away could hear his wail the moment he entered this world. His mama's too!

Wilbur, Jimmy's six-year old brother, determined to teach his little brother everything he knew. But right from the start, it was clear that Jimmy didn't need any coaching in the eatin' department. By the time he was three, he already had an appetite bigger than most grown men.

Aunt Bessie — that was Jimmy's mama — was known as the best huckleberry pie baker in the county. She'd bake two or three pies at a time and leave them all warm and juicy on the kitchen windowsill to cool. Wilbur taught Jimmy how to snitch a pie right out from under Aunt Bessie's nose. Jimmy would give half to Wilbur and tuck the rest away in a couple of gulps.

Now Wilbur always washed up at the pump afterwards. Funny thing though, he never bothered to teach Jimmy that part of the trick. By and by, Jimmy'd come 'round the kitchen sportin' berry stains on his lips and showin' his blue teeth in a big grin. Aunt Bessie would take one look at him, throw down whatever she was workin' on, and go after Jimmy with her rollin' pin. But poor Aunt Bessie couldn't catch him. He was faster than a jackrabbit being chased by a hound dog.

But just once, an unusual circumstance allowed Aunt Bessie her chance. Jimmy and Wilbur were havin' a contest to see who could jump the highest. That might have been all right, 'cept they chose to hold that contest in the middle of Aunt Bessie's kitchen. When it was Jimmy's turn, he jumped so high he hit the ceilin'. That wasn't too bad — it only knocked a couple of pictures off the bedroom wall upstairs. But when he landed, he broke through the floorboards and just kept travelin' 'til his feet hit the cellar floor. He tried to wriggle free, but those broken boards held him fast around his waist.

Now Aunt Bessie never 'spected to catch Jimmy, but she knew an opportunity when she saw one. She whacked Jimmy smart on the head with her rollin' pin. Jimmy, feelin' mighty injured, just looked at his mama like a hurt puppy dog. A big tear rolled down his cheek. Aunt Bessie felt so bad about what she'd done, she baked two more pies just for him.

Jimmy loved to go to church on Sunday mornings. He liked seeing all the families comin' in from their farms with their horses and buggies. Once church commenced, Jimmy always sang the hymns real loud. Too bad, 'cause he couldn't carry a tune to save his soul.

One warm Sunday morning, the preacher delivered a real stem-winder of a sermon. As the preaching progressed, that wooden pew young Jimmy was sittin' on seemed to grow harder and harder. Jimmy started to squirm. By and by he began swingin' his legs — just a little at first — then a little higher. About the fifth swing, he accidentally hit the pew in front of him and tipped it clean over! Then, if you can believe it, that pew pitched forward and knocked over the pew in front of it!! And that pew knocked over the one in front of it!!! People were flyin' everywhere.

That very evening, a meetin' was called. Some of the elders, sportin' fresh bandages, talked about bannin' Jimmy from church. Others argued that they were s'posed to forgive Jimmy his trespasses. Finally someone suggested that Jimmy and his folks be asked to sit in the front pew from then on.

The elders took a vote and it was unanimous. For the rest of his life, Jimmy always sat right up front. That worked out fine for everybody 'ceptin' the preacher who had to listen to Jimmy's singin' up close and personal every Sunday.

Time passed and things began to change. Horses and buggies gave way to cars and trucks. Jimmy was a young man now, mighty big and strong. Despite his shenanigans, he proved to be useful on the farm. One day, as he was loadin' a bunch of cows into a trailer, one of the heifers insisted on goin' the wrong direction. Ol' Jimmy waved his hat at that cow. He hollered at her. Finally he waded in amongst them animals and tried shovin' her. None of that worked.

Sweat washed Jimmy's brow. His hands curled into fists. A bystander might've believed he was goin' to sock that cow. With narrowed eyes he strode toward her, picked her up, and plopped her smack dab in the middle of that trailer. You shoulda seen the look on that cow's face.

On another occasion, Jimmy was s'posed to take some hay out to the cows in the far pasture. With his truck parked close to the barn, Jimmy climbed up to the hayloft and began throwin' down bales. The first bale bounced on the ground and came to rest a few feet from the truck. The next one bounced right into the bed of his truck. Jimmy just stood there a minute, scratchin' his head. Then a big grin began spreadin' across his face. He picked up a third bale and took careful aim. That bale bounced into the truck too. Pretty soon Jimmy had all those bales lined up in the truck bed as neat as cordwood. Saved him an hour or more of work.

As ornery and mischievous as he could be sometimes, Jimmy had a heart of gold. And there was nothin' he liked better than visiting relatives on Sunday afternoons. Just for fun he'd catch one of his aunties in a big bear hug. There they'd be, feet danglin' in the air, all red in the face. Then they'd catch their breath and laugh and call him a big fool. But they shook in their support stockings when he decided to sit down.

For some reason or another, Jimmy seemed to have an aversion to the seats of chairs and the cushions of davenports. He'd balance his big frame on the arm of whatever piece of furniture seemed handy. Often as not, that arm'd give way and send Jimmy sprawlin' on the floor. For years, Jimmy family members were kept busy mendin' furniture.

More time went by, and Aunt Bessie passed on. Jimmy hadn't had pie nearly half as good as his mama's for years, until one early autumn afternoon. Jimmy happened to be visitin' the county fair and noticed the women's auxiliary pie booth. He ordered himself a slice of huckleberry pie, 'spectin' to be disappointed as usual. But somethin' wonderful happened. That pie seemed to be almost as good as his mama's. To make sure it was really that good, he ordered a whole pie. By golly, that pie was just as good as the first slice, and almost as good as his mama's. Just to make sure he wasn't foolin' himself, he ate another pie.

That second one seemed to be every bit as good as the first one. Now everybody knows that huckleberry pie is at its very best when it's warm and has a big dollop of melty vanilla ice cream plopped on top. Jimmy ordered a third pie with ice cream. It too, was mighty good, but Jimmy felt he hadn't had quite enough ice cream. And what's ice cream without pie? So Jimmy ordered himself a fourth pie with two scoops of ice cream.

By then, word had traveled that a giant was eatin' up all the pies.

People pressed forward to see for themselves. Word spread to the sheep pens. Then the canning exhibits. Soon it seemed like the whole fair was there watching Jimmy.

Each time Jimmy ate another pie, folks clapped. Now Jimmy liked to please, so he just kept shovelin' 'em in. A few spectators noticed that Jimmy's face was gettin' redder and redder with each pie. 'Round about the eleventy-second one, Jimmy began to sway. A gasp went up from the folks standin' next to him, but Jimmy was havin' the time of his life.

People had taken to handin' the pies over to Jimmy, and he accepted another one. This time he closed his eyes, a little smile on his face. He raised up that pastry with his big paw. He aimed it towards his mouth. But then, before anyone could get out of the way, Jimmy fell over like a mighty oak in a fierce wind. It took a dozen strong men to rescue those poor folks trapped beneath him. They tried reviving Jimmy, but he was gone.

Although we grieve Jimmy's loss, he's not forgotten. It's in Jimmy's memory that all us kinfolk sit in the front pew of church on Sunday mornings and sing to the Lord with all our hearts. It's because of Jimmy that we have jumpin' contests and eat huckleberry pie at our family get-togethers. And it's because of Jimmy that we tell tall tales.

LINDA MOORE KURTH

Having practiced several arts and disciplines, including interior design and art instruction, Linda calls herself a Renaissance woman. Her writing spans children's fiction and non-fiction, romance, memoir, and wisdom essays. She's received praise for such diverse works as her romance novel, Home of the Heart (now an ebook), and her non-fiction children's book, Keiko's Story: A Killer Whale Goes Home. As a descendant of Oregon pioneers and surrounded by country cousins, she developed an ear for the dialect and humor that shines through in Cousin Jimmy, based on a real-life character of her childhood. More about Linda and her books can be found at
www.lindamoorekurth.com.

Confessions of an ATM Outlaw

Judith Landy

The thrill was surreal, the first time I grabbed fistfuls of cash by the light of the moon. I did it furtively the next few times, fully expecting to be nabbed each time I shoved the little card into the slot, magically summoning treasure from unseen vaults deep within the silent and abandoned bank.

Maybe it was the aura of taboo, but the automatic teller machine proved strangely seductive. Soon I was doing all my banking under the icy glitter of faraway stars, the city sleeping while the friendly light of the digital screen flashed its ritual welcome to the bank.

I had embarked on an undreamt-of adventure in banking, although not necessarily the one my bank manager had in mind when she feverishly promoted the wonders of ATMs.

"So convenient, so secure," she purred. "Your secret password will be known only to you."

I envisioned an incorruptible genie spewing out secret multi-digit codes from a puff of smoke hovering somewhere in the vicinity of bank headquarters.

Trouble set in about two months after the ATM and I became intimate, when I visited the bank during normal bank hours to withdraw a few bucks from my checking account for gas.

By my reckoning, I had $12 in my account. But the surly blonde teller said no—in fact, my account was overdrawn by $40.

"Impossible!" I cried, fishing ATM deposit and withdrawal slips from my purse as evidence. Inspecting these, Goldilocks admitted she could find nothing in them to account for the discrepancy. But whatever the blunder, she assured me, it had to be mine.

"The computer is *very* accurate," she intoned reverently.

Goldilocks' faith was so awe-inspiring that it took all my courage to insist on a computer check. What she found when she peered into her terminal made me rip a chunk out of a glossy bank brochure explaining how easy it is to refinance your home.

For starters, on a day when I had visited the ATM once to withdraw $100, the computer believed I had stopped by on four separate occasions, each time withdrawing $100, for a total of $400.

Observing my ragged breathing, Goldilocks said not to worry. The ATM had this funny little quirk. Whenever it quit in mid-transaction so that you had to start the whole button-pushing sequence again, the computer registered each futile attempt as a real withdrawal. The computer had a foolproof system for recognizing its own gaffes, she assured me, so my money would be restored to me electronically as soon as the computer got around to it.

"The ATM giveth, the ATM taketh away," I muttered.

My whole soul revolted at being asked to accept such highhandedness from a slot in the wall. Besides, where was my $52? Vanished by sleight-of-microchip?

"This isn't banking," I cried. "It's computer banditry."

Goldilocks rushed away for her supervisor, a seasoned bank functionary with the vivacity of an oyster, who explained stonily that she was helpless to diagnose my problem because it had happened too recently. Moment-to-moment computer records, once available at every bank branch, were now hoarded at some distant data center that disgorged its secrets weeks after the fact. Whatever forces of chaos had invaded my account, my own branch was helpless to scrutinize them until too late to do any good.

For the next month, I let my snarled checking account lie fallow like a barren wheat field, hoping that a long rest might do it good. So I was amazed when my next regular bank statement said I wasn't overdrawn $40 after all—only $7.

Why had the computer restored a chunk of my money? Had it rectified an error, or had it simply taken leave of its senses, making money vanish and reappear in fits of electronic dementia?

There had to be some way to test these theories, preferably without the dubious aid of bank personnel or their distant data colossus.

I devised an experiment of sorts.

Late one murky night, I crept stealthily to a little-used suburban ATM. There, I asked the computer how much money I had in my account.

"Zero," it replied onscreen.

OK. This was it. High noon for me and the machine.

I told the ATM in button-punch commands that I was depositing $100—a nice, round sum for test purposes. Then I shoved an empty envelope into its deposit slot.

Again, I asked the ATM to tell me my balance. "$100," the gizmo dutifully replied, like a good child who has done its math homework.

Fine. Next, I ordered the ATM to give me $40 in cash. Unblinkingly, it handed out two crisp green twenties, which I pocketed.

Now, I queried, what's my balance.

"$40," the idiot contraption replied.

I was dealing with an electronic ninny. For a moment I actually sympathized with the addled device. I, too, have trouble with math, and it's conceivable that I could subtract $40 from $100 without realizing that the correct answer is $60.

But ATMs are supposed to know things like that. Besides, if the ATM was this free-spirited with my account, what was it doing to other people's? When blunders like this were multiplied by thousands or millions of accounts and dollars, what grand sums were disappearing from depositors' nest eggs? And where were they going?

Contemplating the enormity of it all, I wondered if some ominous force were at work. Assuming that no evil spirit had possessed the ATM's semiconductors, could it be that these slip-ups were part of some daring plot, masterminded by a criminal genius or by the mega-computer itself, beneath which all ATMs are but slaves?

If so, could the controlling brain be brought to justice? Criminal intent might be an issue, and I'm not sure microchips can harbor that.

Soon after my climactic encounter with the ATM, I got a notice from the bank saying that I was now overdrawn by $47. Apparently the ATM, however dimwitted or duplicitous, can tell when it has given away money it never had.

Since that day I have not dared to use my ATM card. It's a sterner test than my nerves can stand, waiting to see what will go wrong next.

And there's something else that bothers me. As a responsible citizen, is it my duty to report the ATM to appropriate authorities? Or should I turn myself in for conning the circuits off a defenseless piece of misguided hardware?

Judith Landy

Judith Landy is an award-winning feature writer/reporter whose stories have appeared in many newspapers and magazines in California and Oregon. She lives in Skagit County, WA.

Poetry

By

Julia A. Laylander

An Incurable Klutz

I have two left feet that trip me up.
I have ten thumbs and drop my cup.
I'm so klutzy, I despair.
I'm telling you this isn't fair!

I'm careful with the scissors,
And cautious with the tools and knives.
I hope I'm like the kitty cats
Who have nine happy lives!

But still I burn, and slice, and poke
Too many parts of me.
I keep the first aid things on hand
And use them frequently.

Cans always leap from pantry shelves
And land right on my toes.
Doors like to smash my fingers
And whack into my nose.

And so I bruise, and break, and bash
Too many parts of me.
Thank goodness there is nine-one-one
For each emergency.

When I was just a little toddler
"Ouch" was my first word.
So please be kind and patient with
This klutz who can't be cured.

Childhood Memory

Snap! Crackle! and Pop!
Rice Krispies for my breakfast.
Soon they are soggy.

Julia Laylander

After a 30-year career as a freelance technical writer and editor in both the for-profit and non-profit worlds, Julia Laylander now puts those skills to work by creating fiction and nonfiction works of her own choosing. Her first action/adventure novel, Cascadia's Curse (pen name J. A. Charnov), was published in May 2014. She also finds time to compose classical music now and then, and has a few pieces on SoundCloud under her real name. She is also a lifelong, card-carrying Klutz.

GRAY RABBIT WITH BLACK EARS

By

Bruce Lawson

Margret Brunner brushed a loose strand of mouse grey hair from her forehead and surveyed the row of carrots. Satisfied, she picked up the cardboard box of weeds and moved towards the next row when a loud, "Yoo-hoo!" sounded from the other side of the fence. The only person who could yoo-hoo like that was her neighbor, Lola Stump, who lived three houses down the alley. She saw her friend's plump face peer over the fence and cautioned her, "Careful Lola, don't lean too hard on those boards. Horace hasn't fixed them yet." As if he ever will, she thought: all he does is stick his nose in the newspaper when he gets home from the mill.

"Can I ask a favor, Margret?

"Sure, Lola, what is it?"

"We bought a new car."

"That's nice, what kind?"

A blue 49 Plymouth."

"Blue, that's my favorite color so what's the favor?"

"We're taking the kids to the ocean for five days and I was hoping you would feed Sara Jean's rabbit, for us."

"Willy? Sure, I'd be happy to; I know how much your little girl loves that bunny."

"She loves him so much she's been crying all morning because she can't take him with us."

"Tell her she needn't worry, Lola, I'll take good care of him."

"Thanks, Margret. You'll find rabbit food in the shed, the keys hanging under the eaves on the right side of the door." And with a quick smile, Lola's head disappeared and Margret was alone with her box of weeds.

I wish I had a vacation, she thought. Since the girls were grown and on their own, she and Horace hadn't gone anywhere. She looked at the wilting weeds in the box. "Oh, well." And with more force then was necessary, Margret plunged her trowel into the soil.

Next morning, after getting her husband off to work, she studied the note written in large capital letters Sara Jean brought over the night before.

FRESH WATER AND PELLETS TWICE A DAY AND BE SURE TO SCRATCH WILLY'S EARS BEFORE BED TIME.

She smiled, sensing the young girl's concern for her rabbit in the note's stern wording. Well I'll scratch his ears in the morning, she thought, but I'm not walking down that dark alley at night.

She put the note in her apron pocket, ready to go feed the rabbit, when she noticed Ralph, their dog, poke his head through the hole in the fence. The neighbor boy Phillip Marymoor had kicked in that hole the day his father took his bicycle away. Nobody knew why he lost his bicycle, but Horace had a theory. Something to do with what he'd read in the paper about old man Newsome's henhouse door being nailed shut so his hens couldn't go in to roost. Margret doubted Phillip would do a thing like that, but still, the boy didn't have to take out his anger on their fence.

As she watched the dog squeeze through the opening, it didn't dawn on her at first what she was seeing, but as he got closer she froze.

The day they bought the dog flashed through her mind. "We'll name him Ralph," Horace had said, clutching the puppy to his chest. "When I was a boy my dog's name was Ralph and he was a great dog."

Horrified, she watched Ralph, wagging his tail and looking innocent, come towards her a dead rabbit in his mouth. Margret screamed, "Oh my God, Sara Jean's rabbit!" Looking around, hoping her nosey neighbor, Ida Tuttle hadn't heard her, she commanded Ralph to drop it. He promptly did, wagging his tail, waiting for the loving pat on his head. But he didn't get it. Margret, her face flushed with anger, scolded, "Bad dog," grabbed his collar and dragged the shaken, cowering animal to his chain and snapped it on. "There, that will keep you . . . you . . . you terrible dog."

Hours later she sat at the kitchen table trying to think of what she was going to do, when Horace, holding the screen door open, looked in. "Why's Ralph tied up and looking guilty? He looks like he's eaten the canary."

"He killed Sara Jean's pet rabbit! That's why he's tied up."

Taken aback, Horace responded, "He wouldn't do that. Dogs named Ralph don't kill the neighbor's rabbits."

"Well, you can say that all you want, but that's what your dog did." She untwisted the hanky in her hand and dabbed at her eyes. "I'm beside myself, Horace; I don't know what I'm going to do."

"It's easy, Margret, walk down to the feed store in the morning and buy a new one."

She looked up at him in wonder, as if he'd just revealed the secret of the Sphinx to her. "Do you think they'll have a gray one with black ears?"

"Sure, Margret, they have all kinds of rabbits down there. Say, have you seen the newspaper?"

Early next morning, hope burning in her chest, she climbed on a kitchen chair to get her mother's favorite teapot, the flowered one she'd left her, off the top shelf. The one she hid her loose change from the grocery store in. Dumping the contents on the table, she counted ten dollars and thirty-seven cents in quarters, dimes, nickels and pennies. This should be enough to buy a little rabbit, she thought.

Even though the days were warmer, she dressed in her wool coat and before going out, tied a scarf around her head.

That's how Horace found her that evening, still in her wool coat and head scarf, slumped at the kitchen table, looking like the weight of the world was on her shoulders.

"Did you buy a rabbit?" he questioned.

"I went to Johnson's feed store, and like you said they had lots of rabbits, but I found no gray ones with black ears like Sara Jeans."

"So what happened? You look worn out."

She looked up at him. Her voice sounded tired. "Old man Johnson sent me to three farms that raise rabbits and not one, I repeat, not one had what I wanted. Do you know how far I walked today, Horace?"

He sensed frustration and anger in her tone, shrugged his shoulders, and gave her a quizzical look.

"How far is it to the Swead's farm on Millwood Road, Horace?"

He looked at the ceiling, rubbing his chin. "Let's see, from the center of town it's a little better than ... ah ..."

"Two miles, that's how far I walked, Horace. I'd still be out there walking in these shoes if Mister Swead hadn't taken pity on me and given me a ride back to town." She slumped back in her chair. "What am I going to do, Horace?"

The next two days were agony for Margret. She searched out every rumor but there were no gray rabbits with black ears to be found. She was distraught and forgot to prepare dinner before Horace came home.

"Any luck today?" he asked cheerfully, coming into the kitchen. But the look on her face and drooped shoulders answered the question. "The paper wasn't on the porch. Did you bring it in?"

She just stared at the empty teacup in front of her.

"Paperboy probably missed the porch again. Don't get up, I'll look for it.

Alone, she dabbed at her tears. "What am I going to do? Lola trusted me to take care of Sara Jean's rabbit, and our dog kills it."

Horace came back into the kitchen. "Guess where I found the paper."

She got up and went to the stove and turned on the gas burner under the pot of last night's stew.

"I found it in the Rhododendron bush. Paperboy missed the porch again, this time by nine feet. You don't have to take my word for it: I measured it"

She set two bowls and the salt and pepper shakers on the table.

"I'm going to have a talk with him. He knocked two flowers off the rhodie and look at this dirt smudge on the story of the upcoming Fourth of July parade."

She dropped a spoon in each bowl.

"He's got to do better with his aim as he pedals that bicycle of his past our house."

She took a small plate from the cupboard.

"I never rode my bicycle to deliver papers. No siree, I shouldered the paper bag myself. I don't know what this generation is coming to."

She buttered two slices of bread and placed the plate in front of Horace, whose nose was buried in the paper.

"But if I complain too much I know what will happen. I'll find the paper on the roof next time."

She shuffled in her slippers to the icebox.

"Yeah, I wouldn't be surprised to find my paper in Martha Denham's birdbath if I make too much of a stink about this."

She took the carrots she'd pulled that morning to the sink to wash them.

"My buddies and I took pride in delivering our papers when we were his age. There was none of this missing the porch or getting the paper wet in our day."

She picked up the paring knife and gave the carrots a long sad look.

"Billy Perkins, you remember him, married Bess Tillman? Old Billy held the record, only missed one porch in two years. Yesiree, that was quite a feat. Why, I'd give that kid a dime if he could hit the porch every day for a week."

She set the plate of sliced carrots on the table and laid out two napkins.

"There's no one who can top Billy's record and I'll wager a brand new ten dollar bill that no one ever will."

She picked up the pot of warm stew and walked toward the table.

Horace looked over the top of his paper at her. "Listen to this, Margret. Here's an ad for rabbits for sale. It says, and I quote, blacks, whites, and gray ones."

Margret noticed Horace looking at her, his lips moving. She hadn't been paying any attention to him, but the words, *gray ones,* seeped through her fog of despair. "Did you say gray ones, Horace?"

"Yes, the ad says, rabbits, blacks, whites and grays for sale."

"Where?"

"Over in Waterton."

"Waterton. Why that's only an hour's ride on the bus. I can go over there in the morning." She set the pot of stew down and bent over and kissed his bald head. "I knew you would find a way to help me, sweetheart."

The address she was looking for was just a short walk up the gravel road from the bus stop. When she approached the front door of the old farm house, her hands trembled and queasiness roiled in her stomach. She'd been disappointed so many times it took her several minutes to get the courage to knock. And to make things worse, she had to knock four times before an old man with a big mustache and a shock of white hair opened the door. He looked like one of those characters she'd seen in old cowboy movies.

"What can I do for you, lady?"

"I need a rabbit!"

"Sorry, none left," and he started to close the door.

Margret's knees went weak, her heart sank, all hope she'd built on the long bus ride vanished with those three words, *sorry, none left.* The last four days of pent up emotion left her drained. She leaned against the door jamb, defeated, tears streamed down her cheeks.

The old man poked his head out again. "Are you okay, lady?"

"No, I'm not," she answered, dabbing at her eyes and blowing her nose. "I need to buy a gray rabbit with black ears."

The old man touched her shoulder. "Take it easy, lady. You'll make yourself sick with this carrying on."

"I can't take it easy I need a gray rabbit with black ears by tomorrow."

The old man watched her for a few moments, then took her arm and motioned her to follow him into the house. "Calm down, lady, I said I didn't have any more rabbits for sale, but I do have more rabbits. Come in and have a cup of tea, and I'll see what I can do."

She followed the gentle tug of the old man's hand into his kitchen and sat on the chair he pulled out.

"Now you set right there and drink this while I go out to the barn." He poured her a cup. "Sugar?" he offered.

She nodded yes.

After he left, she picked up the cup, but the tea was too hot, so she set it aside and patiently sat. She'd noticed the man wore a wedding ring, but by the look of the sparse untidy kitchen she thought he must be a widower. Clutching her purse, she looked around thinking the room could be brightened up a bit if he hung flowered curtains and maybe placed a colorful bread box on the counter.

The back door swung open and the old man came back in. Her hand went to her lips and she gasped.

He held a gray rabbit, its head tucked under his arm. Her heart beat fast, but doubt from all her failures still gripped her until the old man raised his arm and the rabbit's head popped into view. And there they were—black ears—the most beautiful black ears she'd ever seen. She reached out and stroked the rabbit's warm fur and whispered, "Hello Willy, glad to see you in better health."

The old man smiled. "So you've given the rabbit a name already."

She reached to take the rabbit. "It's sort of a joke."

"Hold on, lady, there's things you should know before you buy this rabbit."

"Mister, all I care about is how much is it?"

"Okay, if you're not interested, give me six dollars and this rabbit, or Willy as you call it, is yours."

She took her coin purse and counted out six dollars in change. She was so excited and happy she felt like giving him the rest of her money, even what she needed for bus fare, as a bonus, but she curbed that reckless thought.

"Looks like the bunny has brought a smile to you ... Miss?"

"Margret Brunner, and yours?"

"Hardy, Tom Hardy's my name."

"Thank you, Mister Hardy, for the rabbit and the tea, even though I didn't drink it. I would enjoy staying and talking with you, but I have to catch a bus. Clutching the rabbit tight, she said her good-byes and hurried down the gravel road to the bus stop. She was careful and hid the rabbit under her coat for the long ride home. This new Willy was heavier than the dead Willy, she thought, but if Lola or Sara Jean questioned her she'd just say she'd fed it too much.

Next afternoon the Stumps came home from their ocean vacation. The new Willy was in his cage with lots of food and water. The dog was tied up so there would be no more of his nonsense.

Margret was humming to herself, while taking the last bed sheet off the clothesline, when she heard a shriek from down the alley. Dropping the sheet and clothespins into the basket, she hurried to the fence to see what the trouble was, and saw Lola Stump's plump body running towards her.

"Call Father Patrick, Margret! The priest has got to see this miracle!" Stopping at the fence, Lola clutched Margret's hands. "You won't believe it, but I've seen it with my own eyes!"

"What on earth are you screaming about, Lola? What's this miracle?"

Her friend's face was flushed, her hands trembled grasping hers.

"Take your time, Lola, take a deep breath. You can tell me what this is all about when you're calmer."

Lola couldn't wait and blurted out, "When we were ready to leave on our trip the Plymouth was loaded with the kids and our beach stuff and Burt decided to check on the rabbit one more time to make sure the cage was locked. Well, you can imagine our shock when we found poor Willy had died. Of course you knew all this from the note I left on top of the cage. Anyway, we decided to bury the rabbit and tell Sara Jean when we got back rather than spoil the kid's vacation."

Margret stared at Lola, the news, slowly sinking in.

"Just now, Margret, Sara Jean jumped out of the car and ran to see her rabbit before we could tell her what happened. But we ourselves were rendered speechless when we discovered little Willy, his grave open, had risen from the dead." Pausing to catch her breath, Lola gripped the top of the fence and stared at Margret. "To make this a miracle for the ages, Willy has given birth to five little bunnies." With that last bit of news, Lola stepped back from the fence, a glow radiant on her pink cheeks, an angelic look in her eyes that could only be described as *divinely inspired.*

"Sorry, Margret, I can't talk anymore. I've got to find Father Patrick."

Shaking her head in disbelief for what she put herself through these last days, Margret made three decisions as she watched Lola's plump rear end disappear into her backyard. First, she'd swear Horace to secrecy about the last five days and her trip to Waterton so Lola could have her miracles to talk about. Second, she would unchain Ralph and give him a bone and apologize for jumping to conclusions. And third she would tell him she truly believes that dogs named Ralph don't kill the neighbor's rabbits.

The Pomegranates and the Trees

By

Bruce A Lindsay

Clay sat up at his desk and realized he'd nodded off. "Damn, weird-ass dreams," he grum-bled and looked at his watch. Almost 6:00 PM. Standing and looking out the window, he saw his new boss, Charles Dogwood, tending a bonfire on the patio near the main house and talking to someone Clay assumed was Dogwood's financier. He donned a light jacket and went out to meet him.

Walking down the crunching gravel path to the patio, he thought about the plan for put-ting the pomegranate trees in growth chambers to control their environment and identify the source of variability in the extract. He relished the new research opportunity and remembered Dogwood said Looseff was the one he needed to convince for the funding. Smelling the smoke and gazing up at the cloud-massaged stars, Clay wondered who this mysterious Looseff was go-ing to be.

Dogwood beamed as orange lights and shadows from the fire danced across his face. "Aha, here comes the newest addition to our research staff." He pointed both hands as if intro-ducing a prizefighter in the ring. "Clay, this is Professor Brousardio Looseff."

Clay noticed dark well-styled hair and gold wire-frame glasses complementing dark olive skin as he felt the strength of Looseff's hand. "Nice to meet you, Professor."

"Professor Looseff, this is Clay West, a post doctorate from U. of A., Tucson."

Dogwood nodded toward the bonfire and chuckled nervously. "I was just telling the pro-fessor that California is a nice place to visit this time of year. It cools off at night so we can have bonfires, and we get enough rain so we don't have to worry about burning the place down."

"It's good to be in a place where there is something left to burn down." Looseff sighed. "I just spent the last six months in Egypt and I tried to get into Iraq and Afghanistan, but things there are getting worse."

Clay murmured with a voice brimming with disdain, "Oh well, that's five trillion dollars well spent, at least for the defense contractors. They've made a killing."

Dogwood frowned and interjected. "Getting to the extract problem, the pomegranate tree is mentioned so many times in ancient literature that Professor Looseff tried taking a different twist in our medical research."

"Yes." Looseff nodded solemnly. "Many of the ancient stories have been recycled and passed down through the ages and still remain with us today as the big black book known as the Bible."

Clay took the glass of wine offered by Dogwood and grimaced as if he'd stepped on a sharp stone. Peering back at Looseff, he declared, "Well, sir, I understand the need for the human brain to cling to something, but I've chosen to go it alone. I'm comfortable being a gelatinous mass. I agree with Laplace, the mathematician, who said concerning the idea of God, 'I have no need for that hypothesis.'"

Looseff nodded with a smile. "Don't worry, Clay. We're not suit-wearing proselytizers on bicycles just because we're talking Bible stories. These stories are not original to Judaism and certainly not to Christianity. They go all the way back to Egypt and even earlier."

"Isn't that proof that they mean nothing and have been just some tin can humans keep kicking around to keep their minds occupied?"

Looseff raised his eyebrows. "Well, many people think that, and for this reason the sto-ries and myths have been ignored by empirical science as the source of any real knowledge."

"What real knowledge?" Clay hunched his shoulders and grimaced. "They're a bunch of stories to scare children so they will go to bed when we want them to. It's a way to frighten peo-ple into paying taxes and tithes so governments and churches can flourish on the backs of the working poor."

"Well, again, Clay, I don't disagree with you, but if we can drop some basic prejudice and assumptions, we may discover something really special."

"Like what? I'm a geologist. What do ancient stories have to do with reality? We all came from dust, not from some—god."

Dogwood rubbed his beard and wondered if Clay had forgotten to be nice to Looseff.

Winking at Dogwood, Looseff replied, "I agree, Clay. It was dust. Cosmic dust from the Big Bang, to be specific."

Clay squinted and cocked his head. "You're not going to spring some kind of intelligent design stuff on me, are you?"

"No, not hardly." Looseff paused and gazed at the bonfire. After long moments of reflec-tion, he turned and said, "Clay, let's just skip all this science versus religion talk and get to the basic problem."

Clay was taken aback and nervously glanced around wondering what sort of argument he was going to be up against.

Looseff gestured toward the chairs by the bonfire and they sat. "As Professor Dogwood has explained, we are on the verge of an amazing product with the pomegranate extract." He pursed his lips. "But there is a problem with its consistency that we can't figure out." He peered into the distance. "I believe the answer lies in the first part of Genesis somewhere and you're go-ing to help us figure it out."

Clay hunched his shoulders. "I hate the Book of Genesis. I think it's a bunch of nonsense. I don't think I'll be much help."

"You're a geologist, Clay. Would you mind if I presented my interpretation of Genesis to you? I'm not trying to be dogmatic. I'm just trying to shake new ideas out of old boxes."

Slowly inhaling, Clay glanced at Dogwood and tried to be polite. "Sure, Professor Looseff, I'd like to hear what you have to say."

"We all know the story." Looseff spouted, "'in the beginning, God created the heavens and the earth, and the earth was without form and void, and darkness was upon the face of the deep.'" He gazed at Clay and pointed his index finger. "According to modern day cosmology, the early universe was deep and dark indeed. After the Big Bang, there were no stars, only dark-ness for billions of years. Only a few surviving protons were spread throughout the dark abyss of the void."

Clay gawked in disbelief. "You're saying that verse in Genesis about the 'face of the deep' is referring to the universe right after the Big Bang?"

Waving his arms toward the sky, Looseff asserted, "Yes! The few surviving protons as specified by physics, were 'the waters', as in 'and the Spirit of God moved upon the waters'. People usually think of oceans when they read, 'the waters', but the oceans had not formed yet."

Clay shook his head. "Yeah, and then it says 'let there be light'. How does this relate to cosmology and astrophysics?"

Looseff stood. "According to physicists, something they call a 'quantum fluctuation' be-gan to concentrate clouds of protons." Making motions with his hands representing ripples, he slowly paced around the bonfire. "Over billions of years, gravity forced protons to fuse igniting the fires of stars that became the lights of heaven. Thus, 'the Spirit moved upon the waters and there was light'; light in a sustained and constant source as stars."

Clay's eyes narrowed in contempt. "This is all conjecture and the bending of facts to fit a story. One could make string theory correlate with the formation of puppets."

"Hang on; we still have much ground to cover. The formation of stars had to happen be-fore the formation of any planets because all the heavier elements that form planets are fused to-gether in stars. A star can only last so long before it uses up all its fuel and then it explodes as a supernova and spreads its dust consisting of newly made elements. Eventually all those elements get incorporated into new stars and they get pounded into even heavier elements. I know that you, Clay, as a geochemist know a lot more about so called 'stellar forging' than I do."

"The details are complicated and I forgot most of them." Clay sighed.

Looseff sat. "One of the most obscure things in the Genesis story is the firmament thing," he admitted. "'Let there be a firmament in the waters and let it divide the waters from the wa-ters.' Huh? This sounds like the usual Bible double-speak but—" He held up his index finger, "if we stay with the cosmology model of modern science, we see that after several generations of stars pounding heavy elements together, the next significant process is planetary differentiation."

Clays held up his hand. "Wait a minute. You're saying the division of the firmaments verse refers to the formation of galaxies, solar systems, and planets?"

Looseff raised his eyebrows and nodded. "The main idea of the firmament verse, in my interpretation, is that of differentiation, of separation into different components. Think of 'the waters' as the vacuum of space and the firmament as the solidification of planets and solar systems. This was the second day."

Clay frowned. "Why try to correlate some old myth with modern science? People in a to-tally different culture and mindset wrote it. Who knows what they were even thinking?"

Responding to the anger flashing in Clay's blue eyes, Looseff replied, "The 'old myth' of Genesis demands a more intellectual study than the over simplification that standard creationism imposes. Genesis is a fabulous piece of literature which, if read in harmony with the observations and theories of science, is absolutely staggering."

Clay scowled and looked away.

Dogwood stood and tended the fire with a rake and shovel. Metal clanged against metal as the coals crackled and the wood sizzled and screamed.

The orange flames of the fire reflected in Looseff's eyes as he spoke. "The 'third day' re-fers to the formation of our small metallic planet, the appearance of water, and the beginning of plants."

Clay shook his head as his skepticism refused to crack.

"The earth was formed about 5 billion years ago and life first appeared on Earth as uni-cellular organisms approximately 3.5 billion years ago. For billions of years the anaerobic bacte-ria ruled the newly cooled and hardened planet. Sometime later, photosynthetic blue-green algae came along and started pumping out oxygen. Oxygen was a new gas and deadly to the anaerobic bacteria that had dominated the planet for billions of years."

Raising his eyebrows, Clay sported a smirk. "You're singing to the choir so far. How does all this relate to Genesis?"

Leaning closer, Looseff whispered, "The story says the sun and the moon were made on the fourth day; however, a literal day refers to the rotation of the Earth relative to the sun. If the sun and the moon were not made until the fourth 'day', they could not be literal days and the creationist literal argument refutes itself."

The smirk on Clay's face disappeared into the black void of his open mouth.

Slowly nodding and raising his eyebrows, Looseff explained. "Have you ever tried to see the sun or the moon or the stars in a very smoggy city on a bad traffic day? You can't see them as individual heavenly bodies. Plants changed all this, and through photosynthesis, plants cleaned up the atmosphere so the sun, stars, and the moon could become visible as individual objects. Thus, they were 'made.'"

Clay gasped. "I never thought of it that way." He sat up on the edge of his chair with his eyes open wide and rubbed his face. "Well, as a geologist I can't refute anything you've said so far. But, so what? It's an interesting interpretation, but it's just that, an interpretation. It's one chapter trying to sum up fifteen billion years. One chapter!"

Looseff peered at Clay. "Have you ever tried to write a book? Paint a picture? Most times, less is more."

Clay stared into his wine. "Well, I'm intrigued, but still skeptical. No dinosaurs are men-tioned, nor is speciation. According to Genesis, everything was made the same, and at the same time."

"I'm getting to that." Looseff rose to his feet.

Clay whispered to Dogwood, "This guy should have a radio talk show. He is pretty inter-esting."

Dogwood nodded and smiled.

Looseff adjusted his coat as if he was standing behind a podium before a large audience. Inhaling and gesturing with his hands, he orated. "Once upon a brain stem, in a swamp a long, long time ago, fish got uppity and started walking on their fins. In our Genesis Travelogue, we have arrived at the fifth day. Up to this point we have seen that Genesis is consistent with the cosmological concepts of the Big Bang, the origins of stars, the formation of matter and heavier elements formed within those stars and the development of solar systems containing planets, in-cluding at least one having an atmosphere with oxygen."

He rubbed his hands together and smiled. "Now, we have come to the Age of Fishes. Ac-cording to geologic theory, as supported by the fossil record, macroscopic life started in the oceans as various sea creatures. Multicellular life arose in the oceans. That birds appeared along with fishes in the Biblical account may strike some as rather odd. That birds are said to have formed from the waters on this 'day' along with the fishes suggests that this period also repre-sents the Age of Reptiles, including the dinosaurs."

Although he was skeptical, Clay felt a tinge of excitement as if he was hearing a special secret, and transcended into a reverie. The flickering light of the bonfire danced on the oak tree branches as the stars shone between the leaves. He smelled the smoke and inhaled, gazed at the stars and his new friends. He watched Looseff walk around the fire gesturing and ranting like some strange prophet and quipped with a hearty laugh, "You're going way over my head, Pro-fessor, but I'm still hanging on." He toasted wine glasses with Dogwood.

Stepping up onto a bench to enhance his theatrics, Looseff gazed into a distance only he could see. "The curtain rises and the curtain falls, and the curtain rises again. Every morning of creation is followed by a very long night of extinction. The fossil record shows five major ex-tinctions. We're currently in the beginning of the sixth. The last great extinction, sixty-five mil-lion years ago took out the dinosaurs that ruled the planet for two hundred and fifty million years. Lurking among the thundering footfalls of the great beasts were soft, furry, mammal-like things. The dinosaurs got wiped out and those mammals took over. We all know the story. Now we have predatory banking, and corporations rule and ruin the planet."

"Banks are the new predatory dinosaurs," Dogwood hissed as he rubbed his beard.

Clay laughed and nodded.

Looseff peered down at Clay from the bench. "So, according to the story...'On the sixth day the Earth brought forth cattle and creeping things.' In my opinion, all the animals mentioned on the sixth day were mammals and mammal precursors."

Stepping down from the bench, Looseff peered at Clay. "One thing the fossil record shows is that evolution is not linear. It does not occur at a constant rate. Evolution is 'punctu-ated.' All plants and animals basically reproduce after their own kind but, fortunately, there is enough genetic resilience to allow for adapting to new environments. All our genes can be turned off or on, by physical, emotional, or chemical cues. "

Clay blinked at the bonfire and asked Dogwood, "Professor, genetics is outside my field, but do you buy into this?"

Dogwood answered, "Absolutely, Clay, this is what's going on in the pomegranate trees. You hit on it yesterday. All the effects of pollution and even microwave radiation have their ef-fects, not just effects on physiology, but even genetically. The genetic structure does not change. Some genes merely get turned on and others get turned off based on the chemical and physical surroundings. It can affect the current physical status of the plant and change its morphology even within one lifetime of the plant."

Looseff nodded. "Yes, Clay, it's called epigenetics. Old genes don't just die, they adapt. This is what you must do, Clay. Don't get boxed in by old paradigms or your prejudice. The en-tire evolution of the universe is based on old ideas that still work." He shifted in his chair. "I think your plan for the growth chambers is an excellent idea, Clay. Work with Professor Dog-wood and order whatever you think we need." He pointed his finger for emphasis. "The entire fate of the human race depends on you, Clay. You don't understand it now, but you will."

"Well, gentlemen," Dogwood toasted, "I think it is time we refreshed our connection to the stars and got some sleep."

Clay stood and raised his glass to Looseff. "You, sir, have totally blown my paradigms away, but I think I see the pomegranates through the trees of my prejudice."

Dogwood and Looseff smiled and nodded at each other.

Clay walked down the crunching gravel back to his bungalow. He thought about what Looseff had said and then thought about his childhood on the church farm in Mississippi. A dark shadow consumed him as he remembered the recurring nightmares he would have to face again.

The Cracked Cookie

By

Karla Locke

"Life sucks," Missy told herself.

At twenty-eight, Missy worked at a job she hated, for an absentee boss she despised even more, her love life was non-existent, and she was eating alone – again.

"Are you done yet?" Mr. Wong asked, a scowl on his face.

Every day she ate at Lucky Chopsticks. Every day she sat at the same table. Every day, Mr. Wong scowled at her.

Missy pushed her plate away. "Thank you, Mr. Wong, lunch was delicious."

He grabbed her plate and stalked away.

Depressed, Missy reached for the bill and the standard fortune cookie. She took a deep breath, closed her eyes and cracked it open, hoping this fortune would be the one to change her life. Slowly she read her fortune; "Love will knock you down."

"Great, even love will knock me down," Missy grumbled.

Depression blanketed her as she walked outside. With her head hung down she didn't see the man before she plowed into him. They crashed, like a head-on collision on the highway. Missy's arms flailed in the air as she was propelled backwards, her backside slammed onto the sidewalk. A jarring pain shot deep into her bones.

"Damn it, watch where you're going," the man yelled.

Stunned, Missy looked up at him. The Thor-like hunk stared down at her, and Missy couldn't breathe.

"You really should watch where you're going," he growled.

With as much dignity as Missy could muster, she pushed herself up to a standing position. Her backside felt like it was on fire.

It was on her lips to apologize, but instead she glared back at the rude man. "Maybe you should pay attention to where you are going. You were the one moving at the speed of lightning." Missy stalked off as quickly as her sore rump would allow.

***

The next day, sitting was difficult. Mr. Wong scowled at her as he dropped the menu on the table and sloshed water into her glass.

"Your usual?" he grumbled.

"Yes, thank you," Missy answered, wiggling to find a less painful spot to sit on.

Following her daily routine, she ate, Mr. Wong scowled, and she cracked open her cookie. Today's fortune read; "He is close by."

Outside, Missy was greeted by a gust of wind. Momentarily blinded by hair that blew in front of her eyes, she didn't see him until she bumped into him — again. The hunk adeptly grabbed her and pulled her in close. Startled, she glanced up, only this time he was smiling.

"You really should watch where you're going," he teased. His smile caused her heart to drop to her feet.

Flustered, Missy stammered, "Sorry… I, my, um, the wind blew my hair and I couldn't see."

"Well, at least this time neither of us landed on the ground. How is your backside by the way?"

"Um… fine, sore," she mumbled. "I'm sorry… I'm late for work."

His chuckle followed as she slowly walked away.

***

Today, like every day, it was the same old routine. Get up, feed Darkone, the cat, grab a coffee and muffin, catch the bus to work, sit at the desk, pound on the keyboard, then off to lunch. Missy was becoming a creature of habit; her life held no adventure and no excitement.

Just as she did every day, Missy sat at her table at Lucky Chopsticks. Once again, Mr. Wong scowled and Missy reached for the fortune cookie. For some reason, today, she hesitated before cracking it open. Slowly she pulled out the fortune, it read; "Say yes." Puzzled, she stared at it.

"Is something the matter?" Mr. Wong asked.

She glanced up, he wasn't scowling; in fact he looked a bit concerned. "Sorry, no, I mean, well," she stumbled.

"Yes?" he prompted.

"Well… it's the fortune cookies lately," she replied.

"What's wrong with them?" Mr. Wong asked.

"They don't have the typical fortune in them," she answered. She handed the fortune to him to read.

With a frown, he tossed the fortune on the table and stormed into the kitchen.

"What are you up to old woman?" she heard him yell in the kitchen.

Outside, Missy stopped and looked back inside, confusion etched on her face. She knew there was something strange about the whole thing.

"Hello again," he said, snapping her out of her thoughts. "Fancy meeting you here." Startled, she turned to look at him, "Are you stalking me?"

He laughed, sending shivers through her, "Do you want me to?"

Missy decided the universe had turned upside down. Maybe she should go back to her cubicle where work would take her away from all of this strangeness.

"I need to get back to work," she mumbled as she walked off.

***

The next day was busy at work. Missy was tempted to skip lunch but the rumbling in her stomach changed her mind. She considered ordering take out and bringing it back to her desk, but decided against the idea.

He was standing just outside the door of Lucky Chopsticks. Missy took a moment to study him. He was just under six feet. His velvety blond hair was styled in an executive cut. His suit hugged his broad shoulders. When she looked up, she caught his piercing blue eyes smiling at her. Embarrassed, she turned a deep shade of pink as she slowly approached him.

"Good afternoon," he said.

"Um, hi."

"I thought since we keep running into each other we should have lunch."

"Together?" she squeaked.

He laughed, "That's usually how it works."

"Oh, um, well, I suppose," she answered.

"I don't want to intrude. Did you have other plans?"

"No."

"Well, good then." He opened the door and followed Missy to her usual table.

After Mr. Wong walked away to get their drinks, she glanced nervously at the stranger. Missy knew she should say something, but for the life of her she couldn't imagine what.

"Maybe we should introduce ourselves," he said, offering his hand. "My name is Michael."

***

Missy placed her hand in his, sending tingles up her arm. She returned his smile, "My name is Melissa, but most people call me Missy."

"Hello, Melissa," his husky voiced resonated across the table and Missy found she couldn't breathe.

"So, what shall you have?" Mr. Wong said, interrupting the moment.

Michael smiled and winked, "I will have the sweet and sour chicken please."

"Your usual?" Mr. Wong asked Missy.

"No. I think I'll have what he's having, please," she answered.

Missy enjoyed lunch. Michael made her laugh, made her blush and made her feel giddy inside.

When Michael snatched the check to pay for lunch, Missy said, "I can't let you pay."

"Sure you can. It's the least I could do after knocking you down the other day."

Missy heard a low throaty chuckle while Michael read his fortune. "Do you want to know what it says?" he asked.

"It's bad luck to tell."

"Oh, come on, you don't believe in that stuff do you? I'll read it to you anyway. It says, 'Lady Luck sits opposite you.'"

"That's an odd fortune," Missy commented.

"Not really," Michael said huskily. "I think it might be right for once."

Missy blushed and read hers, frowning as she did.

"What does yours say?" he asked.

"Oh, um, nothing. It's silly."

"Come on, I shared, now it's your turn."

"Oh, all right. It says, 'Change has happened for the better.'"

"I think we should keep these for good luck," Michael said.

"Yes," Missy whispered, "I think we should."

The sun was out and its warmth felt good on her face. When she looked at Michael she noticed the yearning in his eyes. It pulled her in and she quivered with excitement.

When Michael leaned toward her, she instinctively closed her eyes anticipating the kiss. His lips briefly brushed her lips, then whispered, "Until tomorrow."

When she opened her eyes, he was walking away.

***

Michael now met her at "their" restaurant. He would gang up with Mr. Wong and tempt her palette with new dishes. They sat at different tables. The variety brought out the long dormant adventurer inside her.

Laughing at his clever jokes, she found his wit a welcome relief to her day. His compliments made her blush. She never felt more alive.

The real highlight of lunch was the goodbye kiss. A gentle touch, just enough to tease and leave her craving more.

***

It had been over a week since Missy first ran into Michael. Lunchtime was now her favorite part of the day. Today she took special care with her appearance. Today, she wanted to encourage Michael and convey the message that she was ready for more than just a kiss.

She chose a white sleeveless summer dress that clung to her like a fitted glove. Yesterday she splurged and had her hair done. The stylist cut her hair short, enhancing her delicate face.

With one last twirl and giggle she left her apartment. Butterflies fluttered in her stomach. She just hoped she wasn't making a fool of herself.

Daydreaming, Missy had a hard time focusing at work.

"Okay, who is he?" her co-worker, Marcia asked.

"Excuse me?" Missy asked.

"You heard me. Look at you, all dressed up. That can mean only one thing; you have a hot date."

"I'm just having lunch with a friend." Missy answered.

"Don't give me that, honey. Every day for the last week you have scurried out of here at lunchtime. I could practically see the excitement buzzing off you."

"What's going on?" Amber, another co-worker, asked.

"I'm trying to find out about Missy's hot date," Marcia replied.

"And?" Amber asked.

"She won't tell me," Marcia answered.

Missy glanced at the clock and panicked. She grabbed her purse and hurried for the elevator.

Marcia yelled, "By the way, honey, this new hot look ya got going is working. It's much better than that depressed frumpy thing you were doing. You keep dressing like that and your hot date will just keep getting hotter."

Missy heard their laughter as the elevator doors closed.

***

From the lustful look on Michael's face when he saw her, Missy realized that Marcia might be right.

"Well, I think I just lost my appetite for food, but I think I'm hungry for something else." Michael whispered as he pulled Missy into his arms.

Missy's insides turned to mush and her heart skipped a beat. "Yes, please," she whispered.

Missy was late returning to work and it was worth every minute she spent in Michael's arms.

Laughter from Amber and Marcia greeted her as she sat down at her desk.

"Told ya," Marcia yelled at Amber.

Missy couldn't help it, life was good and she felt like she was in heaven. She smiled at Marcia's remark.

Donald, their supervisor, picked that moment to come out of his office and informed everyone that they had to work on Saturday.

Without thinking, Missy yelled out, "No, I can't."

He looked pointedly at her, "Sorry Missy, it's mandatory. The boss is coming in on Monday. This is not a request. Also, there is a mandatory meeting on Monday at 8:00 am. Do not be late." Donald disappeared back into his office.

Missy shook with anger. Never had she despised her elusive boss more. She finally had a date and now she had to cancel because Mr. Workaholic demanded everyone else give up their lives for him.

***

On Monday morning, Missy felt the buzz when she stepped off the elevator.

"What's happening?" Missy asked Marcia.

"He's here," Marcia answered. Seeing Missy's quizzical look she continued, "You know, the boss that none of us have ever seen."

"Yeah, and I hear he is drop-dead gorgeous," Amber piped in.

In the three years at her job, Missy had never seen the Great Mr. Ingals, as he was often referred to. She sometimes wondered if he even existed. She now felt as excited as everyone else.

"Okay, everyone, settle down," Donald yelled over the buzzing. Only the hum of the air conditioner could now be heard.

"People, I know you've heard the rumor that we have a new owner, the rumor is true. Today, Mr. Ingals is here with us to talk about the transition." Donald announced.

When Mr. Ingals stepped forward, Missy felt faint. Mr. Ingals was her lunch date. Her dream lover. Her boss.

"Honey, are you okay?" Marcia asked.

"I, um, I, I think I'm going to be ill." Missy said as she fled for the elevator.

Depressed, she got home and flopped on her bed. Pent up tears broke free. It was over. Her brief moments of happiness, her lift from the life that sucked was gone. There was no way she could continue dating him now. He was her boss and way out of her league.

Missy called in sick for the next three days. Would Michael worry about her when she missed their lunch dates?

She had to drag herself back to work. Life sucked before Michael, but now it was going to be downright horrible.

"You look awful," Marcia said as she peeked over the edge of the cubicle.

"Thanks," was Missy's muffled reply.

"Did he break your heart?" Marcia asked.

Marcia's compassion was too much to take.

"Please, I can't talk about it right now," Missy pleaded.

"Okay, honey," Marcia said and went back to work.

Missy felt him before she saw him. Taking a deep breath, she slowly turned around.

"Melissa, are you okay?" Michael asked.

"Good morning, Mr. Ingals. I'm sorry, I've been out sick."

"Are you okay, now?"

His concern was too much for her.

"Yes, I am," Missy, answered. "Thank you for asking. May I help you with something?"

Michael said, "Yes, could you please come into my office."

"Of course." Missy got up and followed Michael into his office.

"Shut the door," Michael whispered.

Missy quietly shut the door. Closing her eyes, she tried to calm her beating heart before she turned back to face him.

"What's really going on?" Michael asked.

"I am not sure what you mean?" Missy said.

"Yes, you do. You canceled our weekend and now you are acting like we are strangers."

***

Irritation replaced her depression. "I canceled our weekend because I had to work for your company." Her voice was strained.

Recovering, she whispered, "Why? Why didn't you tell me who you were?"

"Melissa, I didn't know you worked here." He reached for her. He wanted to hold her. He had missed her and had been so worried.

"Don't," she pleaded.

"Melissa?"

"Please, don't," she whispered, tears now falling. "I can't. I can't be with you now." Turning, she raced out of his office. Running past her co-workers, she locked herself in the women's restroom. Huddled on the floor, she covered her face and sobbed.

"Missy?" Marcia's tentative voice quietly reached her through her sobs. "Please, open the door."

Hiccupping, Missy wiped her eyes and unlocked the door.

Marcia took one look at her and pulled her in for a hug. "Oh, honey," she whispered as she stroked Missy's back. "Your hot date was him, wasn't it?"

"Yes," Missy stuttered. "Now… now… I just can't," She started to cry again.

"Sure you can," Marcia said.

Incredulous, Missy leaned back and looked at her. "No, I can't. He's my boss now."

"So?" Marcia said.

"So… so, he's my boss."

"For right now, but soon he will be your ex-boss."

"Yeah, but, well, now, I mean," her heart leaped with hope. "I mean, we were only just starting to date."

"Yes, and now you let things happen naturally and see where it goes," Marcia answered. "But, first blow your nose, wash your face and then go to lunch."

With a smile, Marcia turned and left Missy alone.

Lunch? How could she eat? Was Marcia right? Could she just see what happens? Feeling confident, she blew her nose and washed her face.

When she walked into Lucky Chopsticks, she expected it to all look different. Missy wasn't sure why, maybe because she was different.

Instead of Mr. Wong waiting on her, his mother greeted her. "Good afternoon Missy, what would you like for lunch today?"

Missy's first response was to say, "the usual" but decided to try something new. "Surprise me," Missy answered. As Mrs. Wong walked away, Missy called out, "Just nothing too spicy please."

After lunch was over, Mrs. Wong brought the bill and with a wink handed her a fortune cookie. Missy cracked it open and laughed when she read her fortune, "He's yours, just go for it."

Life no longer sucked. She was going to go for it, and this time she would get what she wanted most — Love.

Karla Locke

Welcome. As a long time reader, I have now explored the world of writing and have self-published my first short story, MY UNDOING. I live in the beautiful and inspirational Pacific Northwest, surrounded by water, wildlife and writers. My business, Armchair ePublishing, provides a service to authors in helping them prepare their stories for self-publishing. Being surrounded by so much talent made my creative juices explode and the craving to write burst out.

As the Crow Flies

B. J. McCall

The ear-splitting "Caw!" reverberating from the first class cabin made me jump. "Oh, for Pete's sake, I'd swear that was a crow. That's ridiculous. Who'd be stupid enough to bring a bird on board, especially a crow?" I thought with some irritation, but kept it to myself since I was alone in the galley. I shook my head, then remembered some of the things I'd seen in my job as a flight attendant. Like the woman who wanted me to open her window for fresh air and the man who wanted his money back because the passenger next to him stank and the scammer who deliberately poured coffee on himself and sued the airline claiming the attendant did it.

"Oh, well, Sue's responsible for whatever happens in the cabin, including birds. My job right now is getting these catered lunches ready to serve." One perk of being lead attendant is getting to choose your position. I reached into the thermal container for another plate of food, humming, "What's Love Got to Do with It?" my latest favorite song. I liked Tina Turner's music better since she left Ike. Another rasping "Caw!" cut off my humming. Probably a music critic. I had no illusions about my musical talent, but this imitation of a demented crow wasn't an improvement.

"I hope Sue shuts up that squawking fowl soon. It's annoying." I slapped a croissant down on the plate, wishing it was that offensive bird. Or better yet, the inconsiderate oaf who thinks rules are for other people. Everyone knows most animals aren't allowed in the passenger cabins, but I'd encountered pets hidden in purses, tucked into knitting bags, stuffed in a kid's pocket; and once a monkey in a hatbox. This was a first for a bird and I wondered how they did it.

Provoked by another insolent "Caw," I decided it was time I found out what was going on and put a stop to it. Finished assembling the last lunch, I snatched it up and carried it to the end of the counter nearest the cabin entrance intending to place it on a tray alongside the others waiting to be served. Before I could set it down, Sue flew into the galley, knocking me against the counter. The plate flipped once before landing upside down at, thankfully not on, my feet. "Ow! Hey, watch it," I snapped. In her frantic sprint through the entry way, she got one arm entangled in the privacy curtain and yanked it almost off. The curtain, not her arm. Now from its few remaining hooks, it swooped behind her looking so much like a bridal train, albeit an ugly mauve one, that I burst out laughing.

"Risa! It's not funny! He won't stop. I can't get him to stop." Her desperation brought my laughter to a quick halt.

"Caw!" came another mocking rasp.

"Who can't you stop and why can't you? And is that a bird? How did it get in the passenger cabin?" I demanded, rubbing my bruised hip before stooping to pick up the unbroken dish on the floor. I didn't wait for answers. I handed the dish to Sue and squeezed past her, careful not to step in the uliginose curry sauce leaking out from under the Cornish game hen, thinking, "That looks like a Picasso painting titled, Naked Brown Bird in Yellow Curds. I resisted the unprofessional urge to giggle.

Pausing in the opening alongside the dangling privacy curtain, I surveyed the twelve passengers, who were watching me, rather passively, I thought, considering Sue's flight, the damaged curtain and the weird cawing. An exception was the weedy man glaring defiantly at me from a seat across the aisle. Unlike the other men in first class who wore business suits or uniforms like the pilot flying on a non-revenue producing, or non-rev, airline pass, seated behind him, he was dressed entirely in black: black jeans, black pull-over sweater fraying at the wrists, black sneakers. Even his messy pony tail was black. I guessed him to be about thirty—too old to be flapping his skinny arms and squawking.

"That's what I was trying to tell you," Sue babbled, so close behind me she was stepping on my heels. "I can't get him to stop."

"I'll take care of him. You just clean up the mess in the galley."

She spun around, eager to escape.

"Sir," I said in a voice that brooked no argument, "you must stop this at once!" I strode across the aisle and glared down at him from my full five feet nine inches. "At once!" From the corner of my eye I saw the non-rev pilot tense as Crow Man released his seatbelt and stood. Facing me, he thrust his head forward, stretching his neck until his nose nearly touched mine, looking more like a turkey than a crow. "Caw," he squawked.

"Sir," I said again, feeling like I was dealing with a temperamental child, "stop this immediately. These people have paid good money to travel in first class and do not want to hear your inane bird imitation."

He retracted his neck. I retained my take-no-prisoners attitude. Faced by an adamant flame haired woman in uniform who was nearly as tall as he was, he dropped into his seat, cawed once more and stared balefully up at me. The non-rev pilot relaxed and resumed writing in his notebook. With the show over, the other passengers switched their attention to more important issues. "How soon will you be serving our lunches?" a portly man in a grey suit asked.

"Right away, Sir," I assured him and returned to the galley, where Sue had everything ready.

***

"Maybe he was just hungry," Sue said coming in to pick up the coffee pot for after lunch refills as I finished putting the galley in order. "He hasn't made a sound or left his seat since we fed him." Shortly after she left, the voice of the captain announcing that we were approaching Detroit and instructing the crew to begin preparing for landing came over the intercom. It felt like a lot more than four hours had passed since we left Miami.

Carrying the microphone, I left the galley, walked to the center aisle, and turned to face the passengers. Rising from his seat and alternating curses with his caws, Crow Man slowly and deliberately came toward me, his eyes focused on my face. I backed away. He followed me until I was up against the cockpit door. Now his eyes narrowed and his lips curled, exposing his teeth. "Oh, god," I thought, "he looks like a jackal." He raised his hands. I felt the hairs on my neck rise and a chill shot through me. He bent forward, and without touching me, methodically placed his hands alongside my shoulders, his palms flat against the door.

When I heard the lock click, I knew the crew in the cockpit was aware there was trouble on board. Over Crow Man's shoulder I saw the non-rev pilot was writing. Sue was walking up the aisle talking with the passengers who appeared calm. "If I am the only one panicking," I thought, "then I need to get a grip. This has gone on long enough." My legs were still threatening to buckle, but, sucking in enough breath for my voice to rise above a squeak, I said, "Sir, you are interfering with my duties, which is illegal."

Spittle sprayed my face and hair as obscenities, coarser than any I'd heard in my four years in the military, spewed forth on his fetid breath.

Revolted, I started to raise my hands in order to push him away, but froze, immobilized by the look of triumph he couldn't suppress. I'd seen that look before—the one and only time I pushed a minacious drill instructor away. I paid dearly that time for my *aggression*. "He *wants* me to shove him away," I thought. "I don't know why, I just know it's what he wants. Exercising rigid self control, I kept my arms down and pressed against the door. My microphone fell as I slowly opened my hands wide, palms out. Seeing this, fury flashed across Crow Man's face, supplanting the smug leer and I knew my instincts had been right. With another snarling epithet, he spun away and stormed to his seat. I picked up the microphone, presented as confident a demeanor as I could conjure up and resumed my rudely interrupted instructions to the passengers, gratified my voice didn't quiver.

* * *

Feeling a drop in the plane's altitude, relief swept over me. Soon this flight would be over and Crow Man would be no more than a fading memory. It was apparent we were descending faster than usual, making fewer circles of the airport. From Sue's expression, I knew she realized this, too. I nodded toward the economy cabin and left to check that the other flight attendants had begun preparations for landing. When I returned, Sue and I walked the first class cabin, making sure that seat belts were fastened and carry-ons safely stowed. On a second walk through we collected magazines, head-sets, dishes and any trash. "Think maybe we should stuff Crow Man in a trash bag?" Sue whispered as we finished." I laughed and followed her to strap ourselves into our jump seats.

Our work temporarily over, I relaxed, at least as much as a jump seat allows, and gazed out the window. "I wish I knew what the captain told the tower. They've really given us priority landing."

"Hey, maybe Crow Man is good for something after all," was Sue's wry response.

I leaned my head against the window, mesmerized by the rapidly rising ground. Soon it was no longer rising, but racing past as we taxied smoothly toward our slot. Looking down, I saw emergency vehicles and airport security cars waiting on the tarmac. It wasn't until the plane made its final turn that I saw the jetway. A gate agent I knew looked toward us from its tunnel-like opening. Dwarfing him were two security officers who, like Crow Man, were all in black. But there the similarity ended. Even with no guns visible, they looked intimidating, like a two man S.W.A.T. team.

Even before the plane stopped, the passengers were on their feet collecting their belongings, impatient to disembark. I took my place near the exit. Sue positioned herself in the passage between cabins, hoping to restrain the passengers in coach at least until first class had exited. When he stood, Crow Man saw his three-man welcoming committee. Ignoring me, he bolted for the cockpit door as it slammed open. Guessing his intent, I moved quickly to block his access. In a glance the pilot and copilot assessed the situation and moved to either side of me, forming a barrier. Without words their body language and facial expressions warned Crow Man that touching one of us would be hazardous to his health.

And then, as if trapped in a Keystone Kops movie, I watched through the windows on either side of the exit as the jetway, like a monstrous elephant trunk, swung past one window then the other in vain attempts to connect with the plane's entrance. Not just once, but three times, while Crow Man, his face contorted with fury, stood inches from me screaming, "You did this! I'll get you for this! I'll hunt you down and kill you for this!" Between the jetway's misses and Crow Man's threats, waves of nausea surged over me. Sweat plastered my blouse to my chilled and itching back and ran in rivulets off my scalp into my ears and down the back of my neck. I held my breath, determined to maintain a façade of composure, all the while wondering if this time he really meant to hit me and praying I wouldn't heave up.

"Oh, god," I thought watching the jet way miss yet again, "what if we have to use the emergency slide. I can't even remember those procedures. A slight jolt shook the plane as the jet way made contact. The exit door crashed against the wall alongside the pilots and me. Both security men burst through the opening and slammed the screaming Crow Man to the floor, cuffed him, and snarled, "Shut up, ass hole!" He did. One officer reached down intending to pull the prostrate Crow Man upright, but before he could, a tsunami of passengers, all 267 of them, flowed forward, rising like a wave up and over his silent, prone body. Pinned to the cockpit wall, the pilots and I stood facing the nonplussed security officers trapped against the opposite wall. As the mass of humanity jostled past intent only on escape, I decided my usual thanks for flying with us and hopes their experience was a pleasant one could be dispensed with.

* * *

"I've never seen a plane empty so fast," I commented wryly to the pilot nearest me as the last passenger disappeared from the jetway. Crow Man still lay quietly on the floor. With a grimace, a security officer dragged Crow Man to his feet. Shaken, probably by how close he'd come to being trampled, he rose and stood swaying in place until prodded by an officer toward the exit. From the jetway they turned to face the plane, waiting for the officer who was taking information from the pilots and me.

"Do you want to prefer charges, Miss?" he asked. Before I could answer, a sudden movement from the jetway caused us to look toward it just as Crow Man delivered a vicious kick to the officer's groin. At his anguished cry of pain and fury, his partner sprinted toward them, stuffing the notebook into his pocket as he ran, calling back, "Don't bother, Miss, we'll do it for you."

I saw the non-rev pilot leave his seat and walk toward us. "You know, Risa," he said reading the name tag on my uniform, "you may have saved the airline a lot of money. I watched how he never touched you. Like he wanted you to touch him first. I'm convinced he wanted to claim you started it and he was just protecting himself. I've heard of a couple of lawsuits like that. So, just in case he tries, I've got this," he patted his notebook, "and you've got my name on the manifest." He smiled. Picking up their flight bags, the three men left the plane.

I gave the cabin a final once-over. "That was one weird flight, Sue. I'm still not sure whether to laugh hysterically or collapse in tears," I said as she emerged from behind the lop-sided curtain in the galley,

"Well," Sue said unsympathetically, "if you can't decide, neither can I. But what I can decide is that if we hurry we can grab a latte or something before we take off for Toronto."

Clay Brentwood Segundo

By

Jared McVay

After three years of tracking and finally exhausting his vengeance on the Beeler gang for murdering his wife and unborn child, Clay Brentwood was at a loss as to what he was going to do next. That same day, Senora Ontiveros offered him the job of Segundo on her ranch. The ranch was forty square miles of southern New Mexico desert and mountain range. The land had been given to the Ontiveros family through a Spanish grant, many years ago.

The past three years had been about nothing more than revenge, but now that it was over, he could go back to being a rancher, even if he would be working for a woman.

The ranch hands were Mexican, but could speak English when the mood suited them, and had accepted him when they learned he not only spoke their language, but could out-ride or out-rope any of them. To cement his position as Segundo, he whipped two men in an old-fashioned knockdown, drag out fight.

Both were white men who were hired by the Senora for their guns after the Beeler gang killed her husband, raided the stock and killed several of her vaqueros. Now that there was no longer a threat, they were nothing more than money being thrown to the wind, and Clay told them so just before he fired them.

The rest of the men were good hands, but if he was going to ramrod an outfit of this size he needed to know the lay of the land, especially the parts that had never been ridden over.

After accidentally finding a small, hidden valley that was filled with knee-deep grass and a small crystal clear lake, Clay convinced the Senora to purchase a Hereford bull and two-dozen heifers from a man back in Kansas City who shipped them out by train. Clay's idea was to raise quality beef stock for the surrounding ranches and towns, where now only longhorns were found. He could see the place becoming a breeding ranch for other ranchers who wanted to better their stock, which in turn would bring in even more profit. He figured this was something he knew a lot more about than gun slinging, never realizing that idea would soon be put to the test.

A few weeks later, Clay's black stallion loped across the desert, stretching his long legs, enjoying his freedom from the limited space of the corral. Clay was headed for the hills in the near distance and the hidden valley with its small herd of Hereford cattle. The entrance to the valley was narrow and almost undetectable. The tall hills sheltered the valley from the harsh desert winds, which made it ideal for what he had in mind.

Clay slowed the black stallion to a walk as he pulled off his hat and wiped his forehead on his shirtsleeve. He was about to put his hat back on when he felt something smash against the side of his head in a glancing blow hard enough to drive him from the saddle. Automatically, he grabbed for his rifle and yelled, "Go home, boy, go home!"

By the time the sound of the shot came rumbling across the sky, Clay Brentwood was face down on the desert with blood seeping from his head, creating a large spot of dark red sand. The black horse was nowhere to be seen.

The two men Clay had fired a few weeks earlier stood up from their hiding place, and grinned at each other. One of them lifted binoculars to his eyes and took a long look at the body on the desert floor. Through the binoculars, he could see the growing pool of blood next to Clay's head. "That's good shootin', you got him in the head."

The man with the rifle grinned and said, "I don't reckon he'll be firin' nobody else."

"Guess there's nothin' left ta do now but ride over and tell Mendoza the job is done and collect our money," the man with the binoculars declared.

The man with the rifle nodded his agreement. "As soon as we get our money, we can head for the border. We'll be drinkin' tequila and snuggling up to some pretty senoritas before the Senora finds out her Segundo has gone ta meet his maker."

When Clay opened his eyes, the sun momentarily blinded him. His head felt like it was about to bust wide open. Even though he'd lost a lot of blood and felt weak, he knew he'd been lucky. He'd been shot in the head and was still alive to tell about it. Very slowly, Clay staggered to his feet.

After regaining his balance, he pulled the bandana from his neck and wound it around his head to stop the flow of blood that was now trickling into his right eye. Next, he checked his gun belt. It was full of cartridges that would fit both his pistol and his rifle, and both weapons were loaded. He didn't know if it would be enough, but it would have to do.

Twenty minutes later, Clay staggered into the narrow passageway and felt a cool breeze wash over him. He leaned against a boulder and sucked in deep breaths as he re-tied the bandana as tight as he dared. He couldn't afford to keep loosing blood.

Clay found a place that would allow him to climb a short distance off the ground and look around. From there he could see both the canyon and the passageway. Clay saw a group of men rounding up the small herd. After taking a look around, he decided this would be as good a place as any to make a stand.

Off to his left, Clay saw a man talking with the two men who believed they'd killed him.

The canyon was like an echo chamber and he could hear what they were saying, along with the bawling of the cattle and the voices of the other men.

Mendoza reached into his jacket pocket and pulled out a small leather sack, then dumped gold coins into his palm and handed them to the two men. "Gracias."

The tall gun-slick saluted Mendoza with the tip of his finger against his hat and said, "Mendoza," then he and his partner turned and rode toward the opening of the passageway.

Clay had heard about a Mexican bandito called Carlos Mendoza; a man, who came across the border, stole cattle and then disappeared back into Mexico.

Clay watched the two men ride toward him and debated whether to kill them or let them go. If he shot them before they got out of the passage it would alert the banditos, and Mendoza would stampede the cattle through the passage and he would play hell stopping them. He decided to deal with these two at a later time. That is, if he was to have a later time.

Clay didn't have long to wait before he saw the bull heading his way, with the heifers trailing behind. The big Hereford bull didn't seem happy about leaving this valley with its sweet grass and cool water. One of the Mexican banditos had to keep slapping him on the rump with the tip of his bullwhip. The banditos were relaxed and laughing and not expecting trouble. One of them was playing a guitar and singing about making love to a woman.

When the bull was about to enter the narrow passageway, Clay pointed his rifle toward the ground just in front of the animal and pulled the trigger. The roar rolled off the canyon walls like thunder as the bullet tore into the sand. In a panic, the bull whirled around - bellowing and kicking up his heels, he charged back toward the canyon with the heifers chasing after him.

Clay's next bullet drove the bandito with the bullwhip out of his saddle. He was dead before he hit the ground. A second bandito drew his pistol and fired in Clay's direction. Clay fired a third shot and another horse had an empty saddle.

Mendoza and his men rode at breakneck speed toward the valley. Once they were back, they stopped and turned their horses toward the passageway.

"Who are you? And why are you trying to steal my cattle?" Mendoza yelled in English with a Mexican accent.

"I'm the fella you paid those two no-goods to kill. Seems like you wasted a bit of gold. And they ain't your cattle. They belong to Senora Christina Ontiveros."

"You are wrong, my friend, I paid no one to kill you. And these cattle are mine; I bought them from the Senora only this morning. I have a bill of sale. Come and see for yourself."

"You and I know that's a lie. The senora would never sell those cattle without consultin' with me first. But, seein' as how you say you have a bill of sale, I would be interested in takin' a look at it. Why don't you come over here? If it's all proper like, like you say, you boys are free ta go," Clay yelled.

"How do I know I can trust you my friend? You might keep the bill of sale and shoot me," Mendoza replied.

"First off, I ain't your friend, and second, I got no cause ta shoot anybody if they're not doing anything wrong."

"If you have no cause to shoot anyone, why did you shoot two of my men?"

"Cause you ain't proved you ain't rustlers, yet. And if you and your men ain't, you got my apologies."

Mendoza stared at the sky while several of his men were quietly putting the small herd back together again. Clay knew once they got them rounded up, they would stampede them through the pass and he wouldn't be able to turn them back this time.

An idea came to him. It was a long shot, but he had to try. It might buy him some time. Clay raised his rifle and took careful aim. He heard the boom and felt the rifle buck against his shoulder as the tip of the bull's left horn went flying off into the grass.

The big Hereford bull jumped straight up in the air and came down running for all he was worth toward the far end of the valley with the heifers in hot pursuit.

Mendoza shook his head. "Now see what you have done? You have spoiled everything. I had thought to let you live, but now I am going to have to kill you."

Mendoza called over several of his men and gave them instructions. As the men rode out in different directions, Mendoza called out, "You still have time to get away and save your life before my men get into the hills above you. When this happens, I can no longer help you. Save yourself, senor. I want only the cattle. Are you willing to give up your life for a few measly head of cattle that are not even yours?"

"When I hired on as Segundo, that made them my responsibility. So I don't reckon I can just walk away and let you steal' em," he called back.

Clay looked around for a new place from which to fight - one that wasn't so open from above. What his eyes found was on the other side of the passageway, which meant he would have to move further back toward the opening so he could cross without being seen.

Clay moved a hundred feet back down the passageway and just to be safe; belly crawled to the opposite side, and then made his way to the new hiding spot.

He'd just settled in when high up on his right he spotted one of Mendoza's men pointing his pistol down in the direction where he'd just been. He raised his rifle to his shoulder, took in a breath and slowly squeezed the trigger. The bandito lurched backward as his pistol fell into the ravine. Immediately, bullets began to pound the rocks around his former hiding place.

Clay took his time and began picking them off one by one, trying to shoot only when his shots blended in with theirs. He wasn't shooting to kill. His intention was only to wound them bad enough to take them out of the fight. He hated killing men who were just following orders.

A bullet glanced off a rock just missing his head. Pieces of splintered rock dug into his neck, causing him to wince, and cuss.

Clay scooted down. Now that they knew his location, they didn't have to see him to make a direct hit. They could bounce lead off the rocks and hope some of it ricocheted into his body.

Through a small opening between two of the rocks, Clay could see Mendoza and four of his men making their way toward him. It was coming down to a face-to-face shootout with him against Mendoza and the four men he had left.

"Hold on," Clay called out, trying to buy himself a little time. "Let me get down from here so's we can palaver."

"What is this, palaver, you talk about?" Mendoza called back.

By now, Clay had almost reached the ground and was out of sight. "It means, ta talk," Clay called out with his hands cupped around his mouth, pointing in the direction where he'd been hiding in hopes it would sound like he was still up there. Evidently, it worked because they began peppering the area with bullets.

Silently, Clay climbed back down to the desert where he crouched behind a large boulder and waited.

A menacing sun beat down on them as time went crawling by. The Apaches were masters of the waiting game, but Mendoza and his men were not Apaches. Clay watched as they jumped at every little sound.

Finally, Mendoza made a decision and called his men together. "I do not know if he is dead or alive, but, we cannot remain here trapped like animals in a cage. We will stampede the cattle and follow them through the passageway. It is our only chance."

Clay moved to a spot where he might get a shot at them as they rode past. This time he would give no quarter. Once the cattle started running, it would be the rustlers or him.

Clay heard the shot that started the dance and braced his hips against the rock wall as he thumbed the hammer back on his Colt pistol.

As they raced past, Clay got off two shots that missed because of the dust cloud. Their returning fire tore splinters off the boulder near his face and drove them into his eyes.

Clay squatted down to further hide himself, trying not to scream out in pain and reveal his position.

Shortly after they had gone by, Clay heard gunfire and shouting, then nothing. He waited, not sure what was happening.

Finally, out of the silence he heard the senora call out, "Clay, it is Senora Ontiveros. Where are you? Are you injured?"

"I'm over here!" Clay called out, overjoyed to hear her voice.

The next thing Clay knew, the senora was holding him close and he could smell her sweetness.

"When your horse came running into the yard and your rifle scabbard was empty, I was afraid," she said. "You told me last night that you would be coming here to check on the cattle, so I called the men together and we came as fast as we could. We captured the bandito Mendoza and his men as they came out of the passageway. Some of our vaqueros are rounding up the cattle and will return them to the valley. The others will take the rustlers to the sheriff."

Our vaqueros? Clay wondered as he lifted his head.

When the Senora saw his face, she exclaimed, "You're bleeding. Why didn't you say something?"

"Ain't nothin' much," Clay drawled. "Those two no-goods I fired gunshot me in the head from ambush, and later I got some rock slivers in my neck and eyes. But other than that, I reckon I'm all right. There are a few wounded men up in the hills. I was too out numbered . . .," he said just before everything went black.

Some time later, he tried to open his eyes, but found them bandaged tightly and to his surprise, they didn't hurt. He reached up and found a second bandage around his head, and realized his head didn't hurt, either. In fact, his whole body felt light and a bit tingly. After a moment he realized he was no longer in the passageway, but in a soft bed!

Christina Ontiveros arose from the chair she'd been sitting in for the last several hours and hurried to his side. "I am glad to see you are awake. How do you feel?" she asked in a voice that sounded like a songbird.

"I can't remember feelin' better."

The senora laughed. "It's the laudanum the doctor gave you. He said it would take the pain away. But we have to be careful because laudanum can become addictive. He also thinks your eyes will be as good as new within a few weeks."

Clay wondered if that meant he would be lounging in this soft bed until he recovered?

The Senora must have read his mind because her next words were,

"You will remain here in the guest room where I can watch over you until your head and eyes are mended."

When she placed her hand on his arm, Clay felt the electricity.

"Are you hungry? " she asked.

"Well, now that you mention it, a steak with some taters and beans, and maybe a cup of coffee would taste mighty good about now."

Tears formed in the senora's eyes as she smiled and squeezed his arm. A moment later, she called out, "Maria!"

Jared McVay

Actor, Writer - short stories, novels, children's books, screenplays, Storyteller, Speaker, President/Producer - Cinema World Pictures and all around fun lovin' guy who likes a good story.

The Swede

By

Jean M. Molinari

It was early June in 1906 when he appeared one morning at the bottom of the back porch steps. He was skinny and barefoot, with his wrists poking out of the sleeves of his well-worn jacket. He was looking for work as a hired hand.

The farmer looked him over. He saw a tall, wide-shouldered frame, big hands with heavy calluses. The bare feet looked strong, planted firmly on the ground. The farmer's wife saw he was unshaven, but clean. There was no dirt under his fingernails; his worn coat looked as though it had been brushed and his feet, although dusty, were clean, too. He had obviously washed recently, and his sandy hair was slicked down with water.

The farmer said, "You know anything 'bout farmin'?"

"Yah. I know about plowing, planting and cows. I can do vat you need." His heavily accented voice was low, but clear and firm.

The farmer nodded. "Where're you from? How'd you get here?"

"From Sveden. I valked."

"Walked! From where?"

"New York."

"You walked all the way from New York to Illinois? Didn't you have no money fer the train?"

"Yah, I have money, but it's for land."

The farmer's wife spoke up. "Why aren't you wearin' yer shoes? Surely you didn't walk all that way barefoot?"

"Yah, I did. Da shoes I save for vinter."

The farmer and his wife looked at each other, then the farmer turned and said to the man, "What's yer name?"

"Nils. Nils Hanson."

"Well, Hanson, I can use an extra man. You kin start today."

The wife said, "There's a room fixed up in the barn you can use. It's almost time for dinner. You put your things away and come up to the house to eat. You can wash up at the pump."

"T'ank you, Missus." He bowed slightly, shouldered his pack, from which his shoes dangled by the strings, and turned toward the barn.

The room was clean and dry. Clean sheets, a pillow case, and an extra blanket lay folded over the foot of the single cot. A small table near the bed held a kerosene lamp, and there were pegs on the wall for clothes. He nodded. It would do. He put his shoes under the bed and opened the pack. He hung up his Sunday clothes; a dark wool suit, white shirt and celluloid collar. His extra set of underwear and hand knitted wool socks stayed in the pack, covering the small purse in the bottom. The pack, too, went under the bed. The small Swedish Bible and Swedish-English dictionary he put on the bedside table.

Ten days later, the farmer and his wife sat talking at the supper table. The meal was over and Nils had returned to his room in the barn. The dishes had been washed and dried, and the couple sat with their hands around cups of coffee. This was their time to talk over the day, what was going well, what was not, and to discuss their plans

"That Nils is sure a worker! I couldn't have gotten near so far with those extra fields without his help. He's great with the stock, too. You know how the cows roll their eyes when a stranger comes in or something disturbs them? He walks in among 'em and it's like he's not even there. When Betsy had her calf, I thought we'd lose both of 'em, but he figured out what was wrong before I did, and he knew just what to do." He shook his head. "He's pretty smart! I'm grateful he showed up. It's going to be a good year, with his help."

His wife nodded. "He's clean, too. Asked me the other day if he could use my wash tubs. I said give 'em to me and I'll do 'em for you. But he just shook his head and asked if he could use the tubs and wash board when I finished. Same thing when I ironed. I offered to iron his shirt, but he thanked me and did it himself."

On Saturday the farmer and his wife drove the wagon into town for supplies with Nils riding on the back edge, his legs dangling. When they reached town, Nils headed straight for the bank, where he opened a savings account. The purse that had ridden so long in the bottom of his pack was flat and limp when he stuffed it into his pocket. He spoke at length to the bank manager, and then left to find the farmer and tell him he would walk home, but be there in time to help with chores. The next day, Sunday, after breakfast he asked if he could pack a sandwich. He would be gone all day "valking". And so the summer went. Any free time Nils had he spent "valking" with a lunch willingly packed by the farmer's wife.

It was a good year for the farmer. His crops did well, with Nils' help, and his dairy herd grew, evidenced by the healthy calves that frolicked in his fields. By the end of September the abundant harvest was put up for the winter, and Nils came to the farmer to tell him he was leaving. Dismayed, the farmer asked why.

"I found my land," said Nils simply.

"What? Where?"

When told what Nils had bought, the farmer said, "But you can't farm there! It's been abandoned fer years. It's filled with weeds and saplings. It's gone back to nature. You'll never get it cleared. You don't even have a horse. And there's no building on that land. The cabin fell in years ago. Besides, it's bad luck land. The man who owned it committed suicide there. No one in his right mind will try to farm there. You've been cheated. How much did you pay fer it? Whatever it was, it's too much! I'll try to help you get your money back..."

Nils raised a hand to stop him. "No, I know. It vas cheap, because it's full of veeds and over run. But da land is goot. I can bring it back. I vasn't cheated, but I t'ank you. You haf been goot to me and I come back if you need help wit anyting."

The following day Nils shook hands with the farmer, bowed to his wife, saying "T'ank you for everyting, Missus," They watched sadly as he walked down the lane to the road, his pack over one shoulder. In his hand he carried a flour sack filled with a fresh loaf of the wife's bread, a jar of bread 'n butter pickles, one of strawberry jam, a rasher of bacon, six eggs and the biscuits left over from breakfast.

Nils' new neighbors shook their heads when he moved in. He built a shack, which they said was an eyesore; it was sturdy, but with not even a speck of paint. He built a chicken shed, and some thought the chickens he put in it were housed better than he was. They saw him in the fields from first light, hacking at the weeds and young trees, digging them out by the roots with nothing but his ax, a mattock and bare hands. His chickens grew fat on the worms and grubs he disturbed and the seeds from the weeds he pulled. And their nests were filled with the dried wild grasses he cut before pulling their roots out of the soil.

Most people shook their heads, saying he wouldn't make it, but a few said wisely, "I don't know. He might make it. He bought the land for a song. If it works out well we'll think he's pretty smart."

With the first frost, he finally put on his shoes and continued to work the land. His hair and beard grew without restraint, and when someone teased him about them, he said they helped keep him warm. When the ground froze and he could no longer dig out roots, he set fires to burn the remaining vegetation.

At last, winter arrived in full force, covering the ground with snow. Those neighbors who truly believed in "Love one another", worried when they didn't see him for days at a time, but consoled themselves with the fact that smoke drifted into the cold air from the stovepipe that poked up from the roof and tracks led between the shack and the chicken shed.

As winter deepened so did the snow, and getting into town for supplies became a major concern. One neighbor said to his wife, "I'm going to see if there's anything he needs. We can get into town with the bobsled and the boys can go along to help dig us out, if need be. But he's on foot. He'd never make it."

His wife nodded in relief, as she moved about the kitchen. "Good idea. I'm goin' with you. You take this box of my canned vegetables and jam... I'll bring the bread, pie and biscuits. I can't imagine what he's been livin' on..." If she were honest, she'd confess to some curiosity, but it wasn't necessary. After all, you were supposed to look out for your neighbor, right?

The couple stood in the middle of the tiny shack with bemused expressions. Everything was spotlessly clean. A neatly made bed stood in one corner next to a small table, two stools and a chair. All Nils' possessions were neatly arranged on shelves on the walls. The tiny stove in the corner held a steaming kettle and a coffee pot, and the smell of fresh coffee filled the room.

The amazing thing was not the cleanliness or neatness, but the furniture. The table top was a solid slab of wood, beautifully finished with heavily carved sides and legs. The stools and bedstead were also carved in great detail and the chair was a work of art! An ornately carved lantern holder hung from the ceiling.

His slow smile emerged from the beard. "It's goot to haf company... Vould you like a cup of coffee? Please, sit." He indicated the chair to the woman.

He served them on carved wooden plates, sharing out the biscuits and jam they had brought. He had four crockery cups and offered sugar, apologizing because he had no cream. He grinned. "Next year I get a cow, den ve haf cream and butter. I miss butter."

They left the shack with the empty box and flour sack and a beautifully carved set of candlesticks in thanks for their gift of food.

The winter passed, and if anyone remarked about the shack, they were countered by others who said, "Give him a chance. He's made it through the first winter. Might be he's smarter than we think."

The first warm days of spring found him in his fields again. Now he had a horse, blind in one eye it was true, but strong and willing to help him plow and harrow. He planted oats, wheat and corn and rye and tended his crops as though they were his children. He plowed up a kitchen garden and planted beans, greens and root vegetables. He built an arbor and planted a grape vine to train up over it. He built a pen and bought a piglet and a cow. A neighbor had given him some apples early in the winter, and he planted the seeds in coffee cans and nurtured them through the cold. By spring he had several seedlings, the beginnings of an orchard.

Everything thrived, aided by his constant care. The pig grew fat on produce from his garden and fields and skim milk from the cow. The chickens multiplied and gave him eggs to sell. When the harvest and butchering were done he had pork and vegetables to add to his diet as well as cream and especially, butter. He harvested and sold his crops, giving him enough money to get through the winter and add to his savings account.

He continued to grub at his fields, clearing more to plant in the spring. When the ground became too hard, he built four small fires to burn slowly and melt the frozen ground, where he dug holes to put the posts for his new barn. By the time the snow arrived, he had a stout barn for his horse and cow, with room for more animals.

Now, every Sunday he appeared at the Swedish Lutheran church, dressed in his Sunday suit, shirt, collar and tie.

The second year was as successful as the first. He planted two more fields, added two more cows to his herd, bought another piglet, enlarged the poultry pen and added a few geese. His savings account continued to grow as well.

Each year he added to his fields, stock and bank account. Some years were better than others, of course, but Nils always came out at the end of the year with more than he started with. By the end of the sixth year he had a fine dairy herd, thriving poultry and pigs, and even a few sheep with a dog to look after them. All of his fields were cleared and under cultivation, and he had planted strawberries, raspberries and currants. During the summer he hired a Swedish woman to can the garden produce so he would have vegetables and fruit for the winter.

As he prospered, he gained the reputation of a farmer who knew what he was doing.

When the price of hogs dropped sharply one year, people discovered that Nils had sent his to market *before* the price dropped. His crops always thrived in spite of pests and bad weather. His animals were healthy and productive. The shop keepers in town seldom saw him, except for very basic needs; flour, sugar, coffee and once, a new pair of overalls.

It became common, if there was need of advice to hear, "Ask the Swede. He'll know. He's pretty smart."

His neighbors gently teased him about the shack he still lived in. "Come on, Nils. You're doing well. Why not build yourself a proper house? Why, your cows and horses live better than you do."

But he only shook his head and said, "No, not dis year, I tink."

At the end of the tenth year, in addition to his crops, he sold milk to a local dairy, pigs and beef cattle, lambs, chickens, geese and eggs to market. He owned a beautiful team of draft horses and had put the horse with the blind eye out to pasture. His orchard was bearing fruit. Now, finally, he began to build a proper house.

It was a big house, beautifully built and proportioned. Again, his neighbors teased him, this time about the size of the house. "You'll rattle around in that house, all by yourself," they said.

He only nodded, grinned and said, "Yah, maybe so."

For some years the mothers in the growing Swedish community had watched him with interest. There was no more speculation. Nils Hanson was a prosperous farmer with a big farm and a beautiful house. As far as they were concerned, he lacked only one thing: a wife.

The invitations poured in, and there was no Sunday when Nils was not invited to someone's home for dinner. Every potluck, picnic, dance, funeral and wedding was an occasion to parade the eligible young women before him. He politely danced with them all, but showed no preference, although sometimes he blushed at the overt efforts to snare him.

Then one night he appeared at a church supper with a young widow on his arm. Elsa Swanson had lost her husband and infant son to a scarlet fever epidemic some years before, and now she cooked and cared or an elderly woman who was dying. Elsa had the reputation of being a thrifty, spotless housekeeper and one of the best cooks in town. When Nils asked her to marry him she said she would not leave her mistress who had not long to live.

Nils only nodded and said, "Den I vait."

Within the year they were married in the Swedish Lutheran church. They spent their wedding night in the new house, furnished with Nils' beautiful handmade furniture and the household articles that were the bride's inheritance from the lady she had loved and cared for.

For the most part, the community nodded with approval. It just proved again what they had said all along; the Swede was pretty smart.

Poetry

By

Bruce Morrison

ALL MY LOVE

All my Love
To you I give
Sharing the dream
For this I live.

The more I give
The more I receive
The more I practice
The more I believe.

Love to live
And live to Love
The time is now
Let us rise above.

Forever the soul
The truth to seek
Spiritual presence
Humble and meek.

True Love
Essence of Heart
Beyond all thought
To be, thou art

A happy glow
This angelic light
Vibrating beyond
Human delight.

Let Love's light shine
From Heaven above
Through my Heart
This world of Love.

NAVIGATOR AND HIS PILOT

I steer a course for my journey Home,
In the twilight of the dawn,
My Navigator charts the course
My heartlight shines, the darkness gone.

I was young and ran off to sea,
I had no sextant or chart.
I set my sail and met a gale,
With only adventure in my heart.

I followed the tune of the siren's song.
I chased the fantasies of my mind.
I was swallowed up in the stormy seas,
Dreams left in ports I'll never find.

I navigate through the misty fiord,
And find the treasured hidden sea.
The shadows in the fog begin to lift,
I discover who I am meant to be.

I listen to the ebb and flow,
I kneel and pray along the shore.
I read the sandstone script of ages,
My spirit begins to rise and soar.

I return from sea to port,
I see Ron's pilot ship arrive.
He shares his compass to set a course
To guide us home, this weathered hull and I.

As I reflect on all the losses,
His gentle voice encourages me to share.
He reminds me to kneel before the cross
For they are no longer mine to bear.

I share the tyranny of Neptune's force,
And reflect on the tragedies lost at sea.
I am guided by the star in heaven.
He charts the course for a journey yet to be.

Now I thank the deacon Deegan
In his blessed sacred dome.
For his pilot light and chalkboard chart
That leads me on my journey Home.

Poetry by Bruce Morrison

BIRTH, BIRTH AND REBIRTH

I sit by the Stream
I feel its Flow
Upstream the future
My past below.

I feel the current
Caressing my bones
I hear the rapids
In soothing tones.

As I watch the cycle
Life, Death, Life no more
Birth, birth and rebirth
The salmon run at its core.

Love is the Continuum
Life is Eternal
In the Tapestry of life
Spirit writes the Journal.

There is no death
Only the Mystery
The Circle never ends
It's all about His Story.

As the stream meanders
On its Merry Way
The Ebb and Flow
A Lesson to convey.

In the Stream of Life
Music is the Symphony
Every Sentient Being
Creates the Harmony.

Sex and Violence:

Conflict, Courtship and Death in the Skagit Valley

By

Robert H. Mottram

It may be one of the most widely known secrets in the Skagit Valley, and certainly one of the most thrilling.

At its heart resides perhaps the most amazing story in all of nature, involving an icon entwined so deeply in local culture that the natural rhythms of its life reach into almost every aspect of human behavior in the valley. It has been this way here for at least 8,000 years.

Yet, like rebar buried deep inside a concrete wall that gives the wall its strength, the presence of this creature at the center of things may not be immediately apparent to a casual observer.

The creature is the Pacific salmon, a subject of legends, whose life forms a rugged tapestry of violence and adventure. But the salmon wouldn't be here without the stately Skagit River, which is both the salmon's highway and its home. The river rolls gray and placid-looking, most of the time, where it meanders between the cities of Burlington and Mount Vernon. More than 70,000 vehicles a day race across it there on Interstate 5, and probably only a fraction of the people in the vehicles take much notice of the water. Only a relative handful of itinerant passersby have any inkling of the drama that's often playing out beneath the highway bridge, right below their cars.

In a way, the Skagit is as impressive as the creature it enables. It may not look so from the bridge, but it is the third-largest river on the west coast of the conterminous United States, after the Columbia and the Sacramento. It also is the only river in the conterminous states that produces viable populations of all of the five species of Pacific salmon indigenous to North America. Not even the mighty Columbia matches that.

For thousands of years, Native peoples have lived along the Skagit. And for thousands of years, the salmon provided them with vital protein, with tribal legends and with wealth. Its annual migrations occupied the focal point of tribal life, not only around the Skagit, but up and down the entire Northwest coast. From the multitude of returning fish the people drew a living of easy abundance, enabling them to devote themselves to art and other endeavors in a far more intensive way than many other Native societies.

Today, the salmon wields tremendous impact not only on Native Americans, but on the larger society as well. Countless families reserve vacation time to coincide with the salmon's annual or biennial return, for example, planning to be on the river or on the bay when the migrating fish arrive. Many families spend tens of thousands of hard-earned dollars for boats, electronics and other gear to properly equip themselves for the event.

But the salmon's impact on society extends far beyond the lives of fishermen. Salmon and their welfare affect the conduct of agriculture, of logging and of animal husbandry in Skagit County in fundamental ways, determine whether the economic development of shorelines may occur, and how, determine whether various construction projects may go forward, and when. Salmon also determine where people may live. If not enough water exists in a particular place to support both people and fish, residential development may be blocked.

Salmon are "anadromous," which means they reproduce in fresh water and migrate later to the sea. Their journeys, which often are epic, have fired the imaginations of men for generations. Unlike Atlantic salmon and several species of anadromous trout, which can spawn multiple times in multiple years, Pacific salmon rush through the final moments of their one-and-only migration and directly into the waiting arms of death, giving their frantic efforts to come home a special poignancy. And their journeys are remarkable in their mystery and scope.

The Skagit is the lifeblood of the county, as well as of the county's salmon. It rises in the Cascade Mountains of southwest British Columbia as a rollicking stream, but crosses the international border into Washington state disguised as a lake. The lake is called "Ross," heart of the Ross Lake National Recreation Area in Washington's North Cascades, where snowcapped peaks tower more than 7,000 feet above the water. The lake begins just inside Canada, and ends 24 miles to the south in Washington at Ross Dam, constructed by Seattle City Light to create the lake and generate electricity.

From there, the Skagit's waters tumble almost directly into Diablo Lake, created by Diablo Dam, and then into Gorge Lake, whose waters back up behind Gorge Dam, both also built to generate power. Gorge Dam marks approximately the highest point on the Skagit that salmon historically were able to reach, a spot more than 50 miles, as the eagle flies, east and upstream from the river crossing at Burlington.

Just below Gorge Lake, the Skagit finally sets itself free. It rushes downward through the Skagit Valley toward the Salish Sea, inhaling tributaries as it goes, on a 150-mile journey from its source. En route, it drains some 1.7 million acres of Washington and British Columbia, ending in an alluvial plain beside the sea that – acre for acre – comprises one of the richest agricultural areas on Earth.

Without the Skagit to provide a place to spawn and rear, the salmon could not constitute the kind of presence here that it has, either now or in historical times.

How do these remarkable fish utilize this riverine resource? Each of the Pacific salmon species exhibits unique behaviors, similar to the others but different in important details. Let us consider as an example the fall chinook, also known as the "king," the largest of all the Pacific salmon. It deposits its eggs in the fall in gravel at the bottom of the river, where the fertilized eggs remain for several months. Typically, fewer than 10 percent of eggs that are laid will hatch, the first of many winnowing processes imposed by a harsh natural plan that lends graphic meaning to the term "survival of the fittest." Ultimately, only a single-digit percentage of those few fish that manage to hatch will be strong enough, wary enough and lucky enough to survive and return to the river as adults.

The tiny newborn fish, known as alevins, remain in the gravel, attached to the yolk sacs from their eggs, drawing nourishment from the yolk while they hide from predators and grow. They emerge from the gravel as fry, having consumed their yolk sacs now, and begin to hunt for tiny organisms on which to feed. In late spring their bodies begin to undergo changes that prepare them to resist the dehydrating effects of salt water –fatal to most freshwater fish – and finally they respond to a signal from nature that it is time to drift downstream. Before they go, they memorize the unique aroma of the water in which they were born, and they carry the memory with them to the edge of the sea and beyond. Potential danger lurks at every bend of the river in the form of mammals, birds and other fish that make their living hunting travelers like these, and the winnowing of the tiny fish continues.

When the survivors reach the estuary around the river mouth, they find that their future is no more secure. Life is good in the rich environment where fresh water and salt water mix, and where food is easy to find. But danger hovers in the shadows, in the depths and in the sky. The tiny migrants remain in the estuary, focused on trying to stay alive while they grow larger and stronger. Eventually they move farther into Puget Sound, and begin to work their way toward the ocean. Danger persists, and the travelers must avoid the lairs of the lingcod and rockfish and halibut that would turn them into a bite of protein.

When they reach the ocean, the chinook turn north, bound for waters in far-off Alaska. They have become mid-range predators themselves now, hunting schools of herring and candlefish, ripping through the schools and leaving wounded in their wake, then turning back and feeding on the injured. Still, survival requires them constantly to balance their behavior between that of predator and of prey. Sea lions, seals and orca whales scour the sea for careless salmon, and eventually these chinook will encounter fishermen, too, with their lethal lines and nets.

The chinook remain at sea for at least two years, commonly for three or four. Some individuals remain at sea for as many as seven, feeding and growing, drifting south into Canada as the dark, winter months arrive, and then north again in the spring, following prey and trying to evade predators.

Eventually, a year arrives when nature triggers a signal in a particular chinook, part of a diminishing population of survivors, and it turns south for the final time, responding to an urge to return to the waters of its birth. The journey, depending on its river of origin, can encompass thousands of dangerous miles. It and its companions will feed as they come, hunting prey and hiding from predators as they cross the trackless Pacific. How they navigate is one of nature's greatest mysteries. They often travel at night, often travel on overcast days, and sometimes travel at depths the sun does not penetrate well. Some scientists speculate that they take their sense of direction from Earth's magnetic field. But how do they learn the route?

People rightly marvel at the lengthy migrations of some birds. But when birds migrate, the young of the year often accompany their parents, and humans – acting in lieu of parents – have taught captive-reared whooping cranes their migration route by introducing them to it behind an ultra-light aircraft.

So consider this: When Pacific salmon migrate, every fish in the migration is traveling the route for the first time and for the last time.

By July, the surviving chinook that are headed for Puget Sound have reached the Strait of Juan de Fuca, the arm of the Pacific that separates Canada from the United States. As they move closer to home, they begin to sort themselves out, abandoning their mixed-stock congregations and segregating themselves into groups bound for different river systems. Every river system is unique, and the fish it produces are uniquely adapted to it. At some point, possibly before the sorting begins, the unknown sense that guided the fish across the trackless Pacific appears to give way to the salmon's amazing sense of smell.

It may seem strange to imagine a fish sniffing for scent like a family dog. But salmon are heirs to a sense of smell at least as proficient as any dog's, and millions of times more sensitive than that of humans. Salmon have nostrils, called "nares," located on their snouts. The nares aren't used for breathing, only for smelling. Behind the nares sits a chamber containing sensors that can detect odors in incredibly small concentrations. Many fishermen know this, and understand that particular scents can either attract salmon or repel them. But the sensitivity of this phenomenon boggles the mind. The U.S. Fish and Wildlife Service believes that Pacific salmon can detect dissolved substances in parts per 3 quintillion. Impressive? That's one part dissolved substance in 3,000,000,000,000,000,000 parts of water.

Somewhere at sea, the fish pick up the first faint whiff of home, the memory of which they have carried with them since leaving the place where they were reared. Its aroma nearly is lost in the vast sea, but like determined hounds, the salmon follow the distinctive scent, tracking the aroma as it grows stronger and stronger. Finally, the survivors pursue that long-remembered scent right to the mouth of the river out of which they swam years before.

As remarkable as it may seem, they're not following only the generalized scent of their home river system, but the specific scent of a particular *part* of the river, marked by the distinctive fragrance of the waters of individual tributaries. They do that because they're heading back to that spot where they were born, where the males will fight for sexual partners and will fertilize their partners' precious eggs as the eggs go into the gravel.

Every homecoming is a big event, of course, and a welcoming

committee usually turns out to greet the fish when they return. In this case, if the run is predicted to be large enough, a part of the welcoming committee may consist of anglers lining the river banks, and others in boats that can cover the water like a naval fleet attempting a blockade. Tribal gillnets may await a bit farther upstream.

The typical welcome isn't proffered only by people. More than 80 species of wild animals and birds feed on returning salmon or their carcasses, including otters, bears, raccoons and coyotes, as well as eagles that gather from around the Northwest for a weeks-long annual salmon banquet.

Other things await the salmon, also. Everything in nature is connected to everything else, and scientists have discovered that the vast Douglas fir forests that cover the coastal Northwest from the mountains to the beach require regular infusions of nutrients that only the ocean can provide. How do the nutrients get to the trees? The salmon bring them, of course. Vital calcium, potassium, sodium and nitrogen that the forest needs in order to thrive come inland in the bodies of the fish, and enter the environment upon the fishes' death. Hunters and scavengers consume the fish and the nutrients they contain, then release the nutrients into the soil with their own body waste as they travel around the ecosystem.

This is so important to coastal forests, scientists found, that when wild runs of fish were replaced on many rivers by hatchery runs, and the salmon returned to hatcheries to spawn and die, the forests began to languish. Now, hatchery workers and volunteers collect spawned-out hatchery carcasses and, instead of burying them as in the past, they scatter them through the watershed the way nature once did when the fish spawned and died in the wild. Where they do this, the forests thrive again.

In the river, the salmon force their way upstream, fighting the current, continuing to sort out the myriad odors and flavors that flow down to meet them, following the distinctive scent of the particular area in which they reared.

Still they're running a gantlet of dangerous obstacles and lethal predators, and always battling the relentless current.

First the sockeye salmon return, in early summer. They are unique among Pacific salmon in that they require a freshwater lake in their spawning system. They move up a river and, if necessary, up one or more tributaries, to their lake, then continue through the lake to the tributaries that feed the lake. It is there they lay and fertilize their eggs. When the fry emerge from the gravel, they migrate downstream to the lake, where they spend the first year or two of their lives. Only later do they go to sea. Without the lake, the sockeye can't survive.

In the Skagit, sockeye migrate up the Skagit River to the Baker River, then up the Baker River to Baker Lake and on to the tributaries above it.

Fall chinook and pink salmon enter the Skagit later in the summer, the pinks primarily in odd-numbered years after spending only two years at sea, and all of the individuals in the run are just two years old. In some odd-numbered years, the pink run in the Skagit can surpass 1 million fish. The fall chinook, like most other Pacific salmon, arrive in potentially strong numbers every year, and in a mix of ages that will interbreed with each other. Both the pink and the chinook spawn primarily in the mainstem of the river or in the largest tributaries.

Coho enter the river in the fall, and fight their way upstream where they seek out smaller tributaries in which to spawn.

Last of the salmon to enter the Skagit are the chum, which spawn here well into the winter. Their influx supports the largest gathering of wintering bald eagles in the conterminous United States, drawing birds from as far afield as Alaska to feed on spawned-out carcasses.

The fish push upstream, accruing casualties as they come, the survivors determined to reach the place where they were born. They're no longer eating now, but are subsisting on the fat that they have amassed in their rich ocean feeding grounds. Hormonal changes have occurred, and the fish have donned their distinctive spawning colors, like birds in breeding plumage. Their immune systems have shut down with their introduction to fresh water, and soon their skin will begin to grow the fungus that is a harbinger of their demise.

The survivors struggle on, dodging predation, fighting past barriers, following the long-remembered scent of home. The aroma grows more dominant as they travel closer to the place where they were reared, each place a location with a unique blend of local water chemistry. Other scents fall by the wayside. Finally, their nose tells them that, against seemingly insurmountable odds, they finally have made it back to the place where they were born.

Home at last! Home to the place they yearned for with such intensity that they challenged hundreds of miles, perhaps thousands of miles, of trackless ocean and all its lethal dangers. In the process, they undertook one of the greatest adventures in all of nature, one of the most epic and most dangerous migrations of any animal or bird or fish. And what reward awaits them at the end of this ordeal?

What awaits them here is conflict. And courtship. And death. No, the drama is not over. It is only beginning. The narrative continues to its preordained and tragic end. It's like something out of a James Bond film, only multiple times more riveting.

Because Bond is only fiction, after all.

Robert H. Mottram

Robert H. Mottram is an award-winning writer who spent more than 40 years in daily journalism as an Associated Press Correspondent, newspaper reporter, feature writer, columnist, chief editorial writer and outdoor writer. He is author of Angler's Guide to the West Coast: Salmon and Tuna, published by Wilderness Adventures Press; In Search of America's Heartbeat: Twelve Months on the Road, a personal memoir; and is co-author of Think like your Dog and Enjoy the Rewards, published by Island Book Publishing. He is a recipient of more than 40 national and regional awards for reporting and writing.

Sunrise at Dusk

By

Cheryl Nicholas

If seniors are in their Sunset years, are baby boomers at dusk? When one reaches fifty, and dusk, what is the appropriate behavior? With one foot stepping, with hesitation, toward the horizon, I want to be a cute young chick ... well, at the very least, a beautiful and sensuous woman.

Experience has taught me that to become a particular thing, one must take on its essence. With a fitness trainer, flowing gauze and a shiny black sports car, I step into the essence of the vixen.

At dusk, should I rather be a matron? Can the spirit of a handsome, round matron and that of a beautiful, sensuous woman coexist? Perhaps, but I won't know until I have bathed in the essence of both. First one, then immersed in the other.

I look in the mirror with the distant eye of a misty matriarch. I can see her with that envelope of tissue that wraps itself around her middle.

Gauze skirt flowing. Hair softly curled, windswept. A purple silk shirt draped over the skirt, dissolves the matronly middle. The soft lights whisper "sensuous."

Fluorescent light and a full-length mirror slap away the illusion. A pear with legs dressed in gauze. Do pears wear gauze? Can pears be sensuous?

In the distance, the deep rumble. The Harley Davidson. Biker babe me mounts the growling machine and roars up the mountain, laughing at the wind, drinking in the green.

High-heeled boots, blue jeans and leather. Sexy Biker Babe. Matriarch in the mountains?

Sexy Biker-Babe Matron.

Naked, I appraise the me in the mirror. Not bad if one accepts being victimized by gravity.

In long flowing gauze, I glide.

In black leather and three inch heels, I strut.

Shifting gears, listening to funk, sailing up the mountain. Sexy blonde in a black sports car.

"Mom?" I look over at my daughter—woman-child .
"I'm pregnant."
Grandma?
Throw my make up in the trash and let the gray dawn?
Do Grandmas glide and strut?
Sexy, sensuous, matronly biker babe grandma.
In this essence I shall bathe.

Cheryl Nicholas

Cheryl Nicholas, from the Skagit Valley, is now living on the coast of Nicaragua, living her dream. She is often enveloped with thoughts regarding the aging process and her writing piece in this anthology reflects that.

Since living in Nicaragua, she finished her novel, Voodoo Bayou, and it has just been released through Amazon.com. She spends many hours on the beach with her muse and constant companion, Cee Cee, communicating through the deep brown eyes of her Labrador/Shepherd.

Again and Again

By

Pasquale

My name is George. The name is self-given, as my species normally doesn't have names. I've a story to tell. Before getting into the story, I would like to enlighten you a little about myself and my species. First like all life on the planet Earth, I have gone to a place we all go after our life cycle ends. My life cycle ended thousands of years ago. I, like all who are here, have a presence, allowing me to view planet Earth and tell this story.

Our legs are short, our arms are long and our bodies are short and stout. We walk on the ground using our legs. With our long arms, we curl our hands and rest our knuckles on the ground, more for balance, as we are large. Sometimes we climb trees, but not often.

Having opposing thumbs on our hands and feet allows us to hold things in both. We are herbivores, eating several kinds of vegetation, including fruits, roots, and sometimes bark from trees.

Our young are born two to four pounds. Infants nurse for two and a half years. A short time after they're born, it's fun watching them getting up on their mothers' backs for transportation. They learn fast to hang on tightly. At about four years, collecting leaves, and other plants, the young learn to build their own bowl-shaped nests for sleeping. At about twelve years, our females can start having young of their own.

We communicate using various sounds, along with body and facial gestures. Learning our language is essential for social relationships, survival, and mating. The male of our species helps with these teachings. Learning these skills is essential by the time the children are fifteen years, and ready to leave our band to join another or start one of their own.

Leaders of our bands, or the elders, have a silver marking on their backs. Being challenged someday for leadership by a younger version isn't something we look forward to, but it is the circle of our lives. Having hair over most of our bodies, except our faces, palms, fingers, bottoms of our feet, and armpits, means we have to groom each other daily to stay clean, except for the leader. He doesn't have to groom the others, but everyone else is responsible for grooming him. We are very intelligent, non-aggressive, and prefer staying within our own group. Life has always been good for our species. We don't have need for much. In time, "gorillas" became our classification.

One day, the peaceful life as we knew it suddenly changed. A beast never seen before came through the trees and stood on the ground. I could only describe this creature as rather large and round, with little blinking suns all around it. We were terrified, for we never had seen anything living that looked this strange. The animal didn't move. It stayed in one spot, making noises of which no other jungle inhabitant of our knowledge ever made.

I and other leaders gathered our bands in the small clearing surrounding the creature. Frightened by the size of the being, we stood a short distance from it and jumped up and down displaying our teeth. Using hostile grunts and other vocal noises, we tried to scare this invasive living thing from our serene forest. Our hostile physical gestures and vocal sounds had no effect on chasing this odd-looking animal from our habitat.

Without warning, two glowing eyes opened, shining sunbeams down on us. Startled, we withdrew into the shadows of the forest. As we stared out into the clearing at the large animal, we watched as its mouth opened. Smaller creatures came from within and walked down its tongue. We retreated deeper into the forest. Never in our lives had we seen beings like this. They looked frail. Hair didn't cover their bodies. They walked on two legs, and had four arms shorter than ours. Their faces had one eye, the width of their head, two holes to breathe, a round mouth, and their face narrowed to a pointy chin.

There were many in their band. They carried things in their hands and walked straight toward us. Frightened, we went deeper into the forest and hid ourselves from them. We remained quiet and motionless. At first, we confused them. Then they spotted us hiding behind trees and in the thickets. Soon the stick-like things they were carrying made loud noises, and some of us fell.

We're normally peaceful. However, the things the creatures carried were hurting us. We picked up tree limbs, and attacked. There were too many of them. Their sticks made more noises. One by one, we fell, unable to move, and they carried us off into the larger animal.

When I woke, we were not in a creature, but in a cave with many small suns. I could not think clearly. Through blurry eyes, I could see my mate, and others of my kind, all tied as me.

I struggled hard to free myself. I pulled hard against my restraints, tossing my head back and forth, growling as loud as I could, but all was useless. The creatures did something to me and I felt weak. My mind clouded over. My last thoughts of being held down, not able to move, and poked at by these one-eyed creatures was terrifying.

Later, we found ourselves in the small clearing where it all began. The large cave was gone, along with the frail-looking one-eyed creatures. We seemed unharmed. Some hair was missing in areas and we were confused. All the bands went back to their places in the forest.

A short time passed with no other visits from the one-eyes. Two of our females were with child. The other bands also had females with child. This was a good time for us. Newborns brought us closer, for the young required lots of work from all.

All the bands involved with the one-eyed creatures had their children within a day of each other. There were twelve all together. Not only were they born at the same time, all our young were hairless, except for the tops of their heads. Six were females and six were males. To some extent their faces resembled our species, as far as having their brows protruding over deep set eyes, a wide nose, and a large mouth. They had shorter arms, and their feet couldn't hold anything. When it cooled down at night, the mothers held them close for warmth. Walking on only two legs, they required almost a year before they could get around on their own. Since they had grown larger and couldn't stay warm because of lack of hair on their bodies, we had to find dried skin and fur from dead animals, to cover our children.

They learned quickly how to create shelters to protect their fragile bodies. When they reached adulthood all the children born, who only resembled us, formed their own band. Like us, they ate fruit, nuts, and greens. Unlike us, they hunted other animals for food, using long, sharp branches, throwing them to maim or kill their prey. Several males would converge on one animal and kill it for food and cover for their bodies. They discovered fire, and used it to keep themselves warm, and to cook their meat. Over a short period, their band grew in numbers, causing them to move into caves for shelter. Eventually, because they had different needs than their gorilla parents, and their want for adventure, they left our home for other unknown lands.

Generations of gorillas were born and died. Hundreds of years went by without a visit from the one-eyed creatures. Then one day they came back. Again, they captured the local bands of gorillas, and again there were twelve babies, six females and six males. This time they resembled us less. They also had to wear skins of other animals for warmth. They learned quickly, stood more erect, and ran faster. Their needs forced them to create primitive tools. Using rocks to sharpen other rocks, they used the sharpened rocks on the ends of sticks as weapons for hunting. Their hunting skills increased by the idea of using carved-out tree limbs to dig a hole, and lead their prey to fall in. They were a more aggressive species than the last. Verbal communication became more complex as their wants and needs increased. They too, grew in numbers. No longer were they a band. Instead, they became a tribe. After many years, they also left the jungle to go to other unknown lands.

Every so many hundreds of years, the one-eyes would come back, and the cycle started over again. Each time, the newborns stood more erect, and looked less like their gorilla parents. The last group was smarter, and much more aggressive. They hunted with a short branch, tied from end to end with twine made from certain vines. Pulling a straight stick back with the twine, then letting go, sent the straight stick towards its target, killing its prey. This last species grew in vast numbers, migrating on foot, over water, and like birds in the sky. Over time they called themselves Homo sapiens, otherwise known as humans.

Humans destroyed large forests to build dwellings. Cities grew, and human population went into the billions. Their aggressiveness with each other caused many wars. The killing and maiming of each other was senseless. Their kind polluted our wonderful planet, and the gorilla population dwindled almost to extinction.

With tears of sadness, I look down at humans, knowing they are the children of my species and their descendants. What went wrong? We raised them to live like one with nature.

Why did the one-eyes keep coming back and trying to perfect, yet failing to create a species caring and loving to each other, and Mother Earth?

It was heartbreaking to see the planet depleted to the point it cried for help. The humans did not hear nature's frantic screams. They kept depleting the planet and ignoring its cries. The Earth fought back in anger, with the only means it knew. Mother Nature fought back with ferocious storms, high temperatures, floods, cold and fires, to clean the filth that destroyed the Earth's environment!

Thousands of years have gone by since nature won its battle. We gorillas still live in the jungle, and wait for the one-eyed creatures to return, waiting for the cycle to start over.

By the way, if you are reading, or listening to this story, the one-eyes have come and gone again, and you are part of the new cycle. Soon you,too, will feel the wrath of Mother Earth.

Poetry

By

Judy Price

Judy Price

ANIMAL THOUGHTS

When will a bat bark,

Or a hound dog fly?

Can goats roller-skate?

Well, they wouldn't try.

    Rodents hate water,

    They never get wet.

    Would a hippo hop?

    Do birds ever sweat?

Porcupines never

Get a pat or hug.

Would an ape skydive?

How can a slug shrug?

    Fish swim in water,

    Don't care 'bout a view.

    Racoons love to take

    Shiny bling from you!

Cats are royalty

And do as they please.

Gators don't eat plants,

Do mosquitos sneeze?

Humans fall in love,

And closely cuddle.

While cows just chew cud

In a group huddle.

Are earthworms from earth?

Loons are not crazy.

Do Eagles have wigs?

Sloths are not lazy.

Koalas don't rush.

Turkeys don't fox trot.

Yet pets outsmart us…

Well, maybe not.

I think we're lucky

Between me and you.

These animals can't

Put us in a zoo.

Judy Price

TRY IT DIET, DIE TO TRY IT

With ounces of air

And essence of spice

We'll eat something that

Will tempt and entice.

We start with nutmeg,

and cinnamon too.

Use a red gargle,

for something brand new.

Bubble blue berries,

And air apple pie,

Imagine their taste,

And give it a try.

Make water soup and

Run a bare bone thru.

Put bread crumbs near by.

This dish may please you.

I'll cook some cows breath

For a tasty stew.

And serve these all up

To a shrinking you.

Cook without effort

No dishes to wash

Share oil of fish

With odor of squash

Edible scents,

like real food to cook,

No Calories to count

You'll get a new look.

If all these foods were

Too good to be true,

Aroma therapy

Could be right for you.

Judy Price

JUST FOR AWHILE

The sweet night came

The moon rose high

And shined on me

Just for a-while

I see your face

And know your smile

Held in your arms

Just for a-while

Wistful dreams

Desires renewed

I catch the wind

Just for a-while

I see the past

And hold you near

You touch my heart

Just for a-while

You left my side

But not my heart

I feel you here

Just for a-while

Words pass my lips

Love once was ours

Again I smile

Just for a-while

I dream of us

Sweet daily hugs

They seem so real

Just for a-while

Judy Price

Judy Price is a Washington State native. She is a published writer of children's book, poetry, short stories, and eight songs of both music and lyrics and has illustrations in several publications. She is currently published in the Internet magazine, "Voices from the Arroyo" out of Pomona, California. An accomplished musician, she sings, plays several instruments including the guitar, violin, mandolin, piano, and often accompanies herself and others. She has taken part in both amateur and professional musical performances.

She resides in Tulalip with her husband and spends time with her four daughters, and their families, who live in Seattle.

The Road from Puerto Jimenez to the Jungles of Carate

By

Abbe Rolnick

Costa Rica is a country of many textures, diverse in its people, land, vegetation and wildlife. After ten days in the central mountains where our elevation peaked at 10,000 feet above sea level, Jim and I turned our rented vehicle south and west to the Osa Penisula. We hated to leave where the Resplendent Quetzals made their home, and the cloud forest misted our faces and chilled our bones, but adventures pulled us along on our journey.

Here the landscape morphed from primary oak forests to hillsides of greenery where cattle grazed and *fincas* of coffee, pineapple, and palm oil produced cash crops. These were lands modified over centuries by the toil of farmers. As we wound our way down, the sun warmed the air, so that our sweat and the smells of the salty gulf air replaced the cooler dense air. We gradually stripped to shorts and sleeveless tops. By the time we arrived in the small town of Puerto Jimenez, our eyes scanned the skies for the scarlet macaws.

Fringed on one side by the water of the Gulfo Dulce and divided in its center by a mangrove swamp, Puerto Jimenez became our transition. We walked lazily through the streets, finding the *pulperia* to stock up on wine and essentials. On a side street by the airport, we found a delightful shop with local handmade crafts and a hole in the wall restaurant where we enjoyed our morning breakfast of homemade tortillas and huevos rancheros. With full bellies, we headed out to Carate, the stepping off point on the edge of Parque Nacional Corcovado, and where our lodge awaited.

No amount of research or rest could have prepared us for what came next. The guidebooks wrote about options for traveling to Corcovado. Tourists could choose from direct flights straight into the Sirena Ranger Station, ferry rides to cross over the Gulfo Dulce, or the use of local taxis and buses to drive all the way to Carate. Written in small print, they all *briefly* mentioned that only seasoned hikers and drivers should attempt the hikes from one ranger station to the next. None of the books described the insane route into Carate.

On our way out of Puerto Jimenez, we made one last stop at the office headquarters of La Leona Eco Lodge to check our reservations. We had booked four nights at a jungle lodge far off the beaten path. The maps were unclear, showing dotted lines that seemed to fade on paper, so we checked in with the rangers. The news was not encouraging. The recent rains had swelled the rivers and no taxi or bus had yet arrived to verify *passability*. Jim and I listened to the news. Because of his hunting experiences in wildernesses, Jim felt confident he could cross the swollen creeks and rivers. The attendants nodded their encouragement and bid us farewell with hugs and handshakes. Within their well wishes, I remembered their parting remark, "First you'll hit the potholes and then there are eight to twelve creeks and rivers to cross. The first crossing is steep so make sure you make a good run to get out."

For the next half hour, Jim drove our little 4x4 down a mud road filled with potholes so deep they could have swallowed our tires. At times there was no road at all, only an edge to ride on. Other times, the holes were as wide as the road and three times the length of the car. I gasped each time we approached one. Finally, Jim asked me to look for birds and tell him what wildlife he was missing. I spotted king vultures, white ibis', roseate spoonbills, parrots and of course monkeys, and with each bump, I tried not to look at the road. Suddenly the road turned smooth and made for a less tense drive, but that was to change very soon.

The first river crossing came quick. We were behind a taxi and followed his lead. The next crossing was so severe that I couldn't help crying, "Oh shit." Jim silenced me with a warning look. I realized he needed to hear words of confidence, not my frightful expletives. We watched as the car ahead disappeared from the bank into the river. The distance to the other side was short; the water level higher than it appeared; the embankment steeper than perceived. I had rolled my window up, but Jim's remained open. Water crested over our hood and splashed inside the window. Jim concentrated on his driving. He suppressed the urge to gun the motor, which would have flooded the engine and pushed the accelerator with steady pressure. Despite the sputters and coughs, we made it up the bank to the other side. Neither of us said a word.

I know now why the map showed the road to Carate as a dotted line.

The space between each line was a pothole, creek, or river crossing. Real roads continue without breaks. The road to Carate wasn't a road, but a series of holes united by mud and asphalt. The next few river crossings were uneventful, lulling us back to feeling confident about proceeding. Then Jim made the mistake of asking a local taxi driver his opinion of the roads ahead and if he thought that we would make it across the river. He advised us to turn back. Shaken but undeterred, we forged ahead to another large crossing. Jim walked through the river to determine the depth and strength of the water, and to see if there were submerged rocks in our path. While he explored, I brushed off the cobwebs from my Spanish speaking days and asked the property owner, who was relaxing on the porch of his small wooden hut, his opinion.

With a look of compassion, he told me we could cross the river using the path his horse follows. Jim and I warily followed him back into the woods to another opening further up the river. His horse nonchalantly nibbled at the grass. Jim surveyed the opening. To cross here put us in shallower water, but a hundred yards away from the road. After witnessing a motorcyclist, with a chainsaw tied to his back seat, cross the river from the shallower spot, Jim and I hopped back in our car and followed suit.

As our car glided down toward the river, I kept my mouth shut and my eyes on the bank ahead. Jim steered the car, judging the current's pull, until we were safe on the other side. I glanced back at the property owner. He waved his goodbyes and settled back in his post on the porch. From this point on, I thought for sure the worst was behind us. I mentally counted and I hadn't arrived at the number twelve.

Without the encouragement from another set of strangers, Jim and I would almost have turned back. The last of the crossings was a double crossing. The road ended, the river started, a narrow sandbar began, and then the river rushed forward. This was a hundred and fifty-foot wide river, with many channels. I watched as Jim lifted his pants up over his knees and waded across. I saw the swift current flowing on the other side of the sandbar. Jim returned to the car and stated that this was the end of the line. We would have to wait for the river to recede or go back. I paced back and forth, knowing that when Jim said no way, he meant it. Then from the other side of the river, we watched as a large black truck easily maneuvered across. I waved the guys down and asked their opinion, "*Crees que podemos cruzar el rio con nuestro* 4x4?" (Do you think we can cross the river with our small 4x4?) The trio nodded yes, and added that they had seen us cross the hardest spots, and this part should be a piece of cake.

Jim remained unconvinced. The men dismounted from their truck. They told us to go for it, and if by chance we got stuck they would rescue us. Jim relented and off we went. The first part of the crossing was simple, but as we drove over the sandbar into a deeper and swifter channel, I could already feel the pull of the river's current. Jim's eyes had lost their blue twinkle; his cheeks were tight in concentration, and his hands gripped the steering wheel. Miraculously the motor and tires countered the current's pull and in minutes, we were across, safe on dry land. We heard a congratulatory toot from our Costa Rican Angels. Jim honked back and off we went to the end of the dotted-line road.

After two hours, we stumbled out of the 4x4, stiff from tensing our muscles at each pothole and large crossing. Sighing with relief, we approached the wooden building where a crusty bearded gringo sat on a rocking chair. This was Glen, the guardian of our car for the next four nights while we were at the tented lodge. In a flurry of talk, he hurried us off for the walk along the beach to our destination. Our luggage remained with him until the horse and cart could retrieve it at low tide. With the tide rising quickly, we figured we had about an hour before the beach disappeared.

Jim split our wine stash between our backpacks. Loaded down with the other essentials, we headed out towards the sun and sand. I thought our walk on the beach would be an easy stroll until we came upon another river to forge. Swelled with the last two days of rain and the incoming tide, the river rushed at us. I looked at Jim to verify our approach and he smiled and extended his arm. Handholding wouldn't do. Instead, Jim placed his hand above my wrist and I did the same on his arm. Locked together, we supported one another and battled the current. While the water came up to Jim's thighs, it came up to my waist. The slippery rocks made poor stepping-stones, but the water cleansed and cooled the sweat from our bodies. We trekked along the beach for what seemed miles, until we spotted, on a lonely stopping post, a sign that read, "Welcome to La Leona Lodge."

Adrian, the owner of the lodge, stood high above the beach waving us up the wooden steps to take us to our tent. Glen had radioed him from his rocking-chair post that we were on our way. To calm our frazzled nerves, Adrian made us Pina Coladas. We sat at the bar, unable to move, enjoying the salt spray from the Pacific Ocean as a torrential downpour swept over the lodge. We were fortunate to have arrived early. The other guests and the horse cart slogged through the rain in the dark.

From our tent, we watched pelicans swoosh down along the waves, synchronizing their plunges for fish. We listened to howler monkeys, scarlet macaws, the waves and the rain. Our quarters merged the rustic with the elegant, living simultaneously inside and outside. The bamboo walls of the bathroom and shower were attached at the back of the platform tent. A coconut shell formed the shower-head.

That first night, the treacherous drive in still clung to us. We watched the rain and could only imagine the swelled rivers on our return. Haunted by the thought of a much worse return, Jim drank more than his share of Pina Coladas and red wine. He even promised the spirit world that if the rain ceased and if the rivers receded, he would gladly turn vegetarian as to further reduce his impact on the land. By morning, the sun rose with a spectacular orange glow and the preceding day was forgotten.

Hikes into the Parque Nacional Corcovado revealed a three-toed sloth entwined upside down on a tree branch, families of white-faced capuchin monkeys, spider monkeys, squirrel monkeys, anteaters, and a family of agoutis, which looked like short–eared chestnut-brown rabbits. A group of coatimundis with thick bushy tails and pointed noses raided our tent, rifling through our bags in search of food. One night we slept up in Monkey Camp where the tents were nestled high up in forest canopy. Small black and green poison dart frogs hid inside tree crevices. Our evening entertainment was watching a mother squirrel monkey with her small baby, swing through the branches above, aided only by their long narrow tails. Hand-over-hand they traveled, bringing their children safely across the forest.

On the day of our return, the sun heated our backs and the pelicans played just offshore. We walked along the beach unencumbered as the horse and cart carried our luggage and packs. The low tide lapped the beach. The rivers shriveled to a trickle. Our past nightmare of driving through the dotted lines of twelve creeks and rivers felt imagined. The huge potholes, now empty of water, reminded us of our breathtaking adventure. Jim searched the horizon for birds and mentioned our freezer stocked with elk meat from hunting trips back home. I smiled at his dilemma, thankful for the spirits who kept us safe.

Abbe Rolnick

Abbe Rolnick lives on twenty acres in Skagit Valley, WA. Her first novel, River of Angels, stems from her experiences in Puerto Rico. Color of Lies, her second novel, brings the reader to the Pacific Northwest where she blends stories from island life with those of characters in Skagit Valley. Her short stories and travel pieces have appeared in small press magazines, and have won honorary mention by Writer's Digest. Owner of Sedro Publishing and a health food restaurant in Bellingham, WA, her next novel, Founding Stones, will be the third in the series.

Poetry

By

Mary Ann Schradi

Things I forgot that I loved...

Hard cold seats in a freezing choir room practicing for *The Messiah* with other dedicated singers, who are also freezing but lighting up the room with their song...

The tear in the old orangey-brown carpet in my ancient classroom that the teenagers trudge upon each day, making it larger, but also making my day so enjoyable with their jokes and good humor...

Wearing a warm, snuggly coat I call my blanket and gazing at the stars on a cold clear night in the middle of December...

Petting my cats in the dark as they take turns surrounding me as I drift off to sleep. I can feel the indentations in their ears and the cricks in their tails, knowing which cat is which. Picking up the toys and odds and ends that my grandsons have scattered all over my house when they last visited. As I do so, I relish the memories that have just been created...

My mother's old aprons that I came across in a box, worn and tattered and patched. I remember my mother, Anna, canning peaches in them and cooking us wonderful meals on a shoestring and I cannot throw them out...

Tea leaves, which remind me of my mother telling me my fortune when I was little. Despite our family being very poor, somehow that simple act comforted me, assuring me life would get better...

Iced tea with mint—fresh mint that my brothers used to joke about—they said that all the dogs in the neighborhood fertilized it so well that it grew and grew and we were never without it...

Books that are tattered and torn and tell a story in addition to the one the author created... Jumping into the water after a long cold winter—May 30th was always the day to begin the marvelously warm and sunny summer season...

My great aunt's back bedroom window—Aunt Rose's cat, Sherry, used it as a door to get in and out of her house. Now my cats do the same thing, and I chuckle...

Catching snowflakes on my tongue and letting them fall on my eyelashes and nose, wishing the snowflakes would last forever—and in my dreams, they do.

Poetry by Mary Ann Schradi

I Knew You When…

When I was a child, I knew you…
I knew you when you were beautiful and joyful
And full of hope and good cheer—
And you loved me as your own
And you spoiled me as your own…

I knew you when my father died
And you took me shopping
For a blue dress and socks, for patent leather shoes
And a straw hat with matching purse for my daddy's funeral
And you made me feel special and wanted
When everyone else around ignored me—and put me in a box and told me to stay put
Out of sight, quiet, still…
You let me be free to roam and smell the outdoors
And you helped me
Through the scent of beautiful flowers that led to my father's coffin.
I knew you when I was eleven…
And you listened to me and told me I'd grow up into a woman soon…
You gave me hope that I would not always be a gangly tomboy
chasing after my brothers…
and causing trouble…

I knew you when you spoke Hungarian with my mother and your other sisters
And together, you would laugh and cry and nod your heads—
Sharing secret thoughts and ideas that I tried to decipher…

I knew you when…
I was in high school—and your son, Bobby, was my confidant…
We'd play old Elvis Presley records in your upstairs apartment
And you'd make us supper—and my mom and you would chat
And Bobby and I would sing along and dream…

I knew you when the thread of your quilt started unraveling
And your daughter left you to live with her long-lost dad–your husband—
Who deserted your home and you in years past
I knew you when your mind–fragile from wear and emotional turmoil—
Stopped fighting despair and gave into the void that surrounded you...
And no doctor listened
And no one saw you or heard you sink lower and lower...

I remember when your son, Bob, was stationed in Korea
And your hands grasped the edge of the precipice...

Our family—My mother, your sisters, my brothers and me, loved you.
We tried to catch you, but you hung out of our grasp...
Our arms could not reach you...
They were not long enough to catch you...
And you were gone...

I knew you when you were in the hospital...
And you felt safe and secure and had no desire to leave...
No one hurt you here—
No one could leave you.
There was no one left to hurt you...
I knew you when Bob came home from the service to visit you,
But you were not the same...
The distance remained between mother and son
And there you were and there he was...
And life became separate for both of you...
And for you and me and my mother, brothers and your sisters...

I knew you when you aged gracefully in a nursing home
Where you had privileges to go outside
But turned down the opportunity to go into the outside world—
A world that had become too cold, too far away...

And you stayed inside—pushing the wheelchairs for folks unable to walk—
And spread your cheer to other patients
Which you used to shower on me, when I was young
And you were young and beautiful...

And I think today... how fortunate I am
To have known you... and that now... now that you are gone
It was a grace that I knew you...
When you were young and oh so beautiful...
And in my mind and heart and soul, you are oh so beautiful...
And I can see you and my mother chatting in Hungarian—
Waiting for Bobby and me...
To come for supper.

Mary Ann Schradi

A Spirit Song of Body and Soul

When I was a little child
My mother took me aside
And said:
"Don't be afraid, chil'
An' don't be shy
You got the rhythm an' you got the style
No need to worry, chil'
No need to cry
Hold your head up when things get you down
An' be what you wanna be and don't ever frown
An' sing with me here for a little while
As we walk together this lonesome mile.

Yes, I've got my Body and I've got my Soul
Don't need to worry, 'cause I'm in control
When Life gets me weary and troubles abound
I've got my music and I've got my sound."

Now I'm older and I know what she means
I've see the troubles, the troubles she's seen
I've seen the evil and I've seen the good
I just don't worry 'cause I understood
When you're down and feeling so low
Life throws you raindrops when you just want snow
The sun don't shine on your face any more
And troubles surround you and enter your door
But no need to worry and no need for pain,
I listen to Mama's words ... I don't go insane.

"Don't need no worries 'cause I'm in control
I've got my Body and I've got my Soul
When Life gets weary and troubles abound,
I've got my music and I've got my sound."

Mama told me the choices I make, will
Carry me through—to the places I'll take
I can choose goodness or I can choose bad
I can choose happiness or I can be sad
I am a leader or I am a tool
I'm a crusader or I am a fool
Don't need nobody to tell me I'm cool
I can be somebody or I can just lose...

'Cause I've got my Body and I've got my Soul
I've got my rhythm and I'm in control
I've got my fingers and I've got my toes,
I dance to the music and sing out my lows
I've got my smile all over my face
I've got my inspiration; I've got my grace
And I'm gonna give all to the whole human race...

"'Cause I've got my Body and I've got my Soul
I've got my music and I'm in control
Yes, chil', I've got my verses that I'm gonna sing
An' when you hear those angels shout, it's me that they bring!"

Yes, Mama! I hear you singing!
And don't you worry none,
"Cause I've got my Body and I've got my Soul
I'm in control now, I know how it's done.
I've got my Body and I've got my Soul...
I will be strong now, as you open those gates,
For I've got my Body and I've got my Soul...

Mary Ann Mimzi Schradi

Mary Ann Mimzi Schradi interweaves experience and imagination to create stories and poems, adding color by including travel, love of nature and participation in the arts. She appreciates the evergreens, cliffs, mountains and wildlife that signify the Puget Sound area. She relishes hiking on the beach with her Cairn terrier and cherishes her family and friends on both East and West Coasts, as well as her involvement in the Skagit Valley Chorale and the Stanwood-Camano Chorale. Her novel, PsyChic in Seattle, is available on-line and in bookstores. Its sequel, Frantic in Fiji, will be released in 2015.

The House

By

Robbie Shinn

I sat in the agent's car watching the scenery pass by. It seemed to take forever to get up the long hill from the town, down by the river, but our real estate agent finally turned onto a private lane. The descent led toward a huge house near a small stream in the foothills of the Cascades. After having searched for property on our own for over a year without any results, I suggested to Husband, who enjoyed wandering like Abraham in the desert, to get an agent. So we did.

The first view I had of the house caught my attention, but there was a strange feel about it as well. It gave me the willies. This antithesis surprised me. The agent pulled into the long driveway and stopped the car. As I gazed at the exterior, I realized this house was in great need of TLC. It was huge. It wanted painting badly and the white X's in all the windows screamed 1970 chalet.

As we walked the perimeter of the house in the soggy, March grass we imagined potential everywhere. Bramble bushes filled the swamp next to the stream. The woods were thick with underbrush of ferns and salmonberry. Neighbors' houses you could not see.

The building itself had fairly nice lines, but Husband was taken by the stream, as well as the two acres— room for building a shop. The latter was the deciding factor for him. Most of the wooded property was on the other side of the creek. This offered privacy and a home for the denizens of the area. Coyote, raccoon, deer and bear were known visitors. I was told an occasional cougar would appear as well. It didn't take much convincing to get my approval. I liked the elbow room.

As we ventured into the big house through the back door, we found the laundry room. To the left was a tiny L-shaped kitchen, dim and gloomy with greasy cabinets and woodwork painted a dark, dismal brown. It was depressing. I was about to veto this place when I noticed a door leading to a small porch. In my mind, I saw this as part of the kitchen.

To the right of the laundry was another room and the only working bathroom. Next to it was the garage. I glanced around and my heart sank. The amount of work it would take to get this place to our liking was immense.

Bravely, we continued to the interior of the house and saw a fair sized living room with a mica stone faced fireplace—another relic of the '70's. The firebox held a pellet stove that would have to go. The floor to ceiling windows faced the stream. The stairs to the second floor were off the front entry, next to the living room. There was no railing. The front door, nailed shut, revealed a drop-off to the ground. The front porch had never been built. A huge gap at the bottom of the door let in cold air and beasties. On the other side of the stairs, there was an unfinished bathroom. Nothing in it worked.

We followed the agent up the stairs to explore the three unfinished rooms and an area for a bath and walk-in shower. A door led to a porch from which we entered a huge room above a two- car garage. It smelled awful, residue of an abattoir. Rumor had it, this room was used to skin bear. Ugh. This would become our Arts and Crap room.

Nothing in this house had ever been completed. Bare wallboard and sub floor abounded. Spiders that made this their home in nooks and crannies were plentiful. The dirty walls were disheartening. Despite its condition, this is the house Husband wanted as his retirement project. This would keep his architectural juices flowing. Ahhh me.

Our agent, noticing our wrinkled noses, told us the original builder's wife had died and the old man had lost interest in finishing. The second owner raised six kids here with one working bath, leaky dishwasher, and mattresses on the floor. He did nothing to improve the place, except let the sink run over and stain ceiling and floor. That man was fifty, but had kidney failure and was forced to sell his house. He died shortly after.

We went home to think about this, and after considerable deliberation, we decided to buy the old albatross and immediately set to work tearing the place apart. The house was uninhabitable. I couldn't handle the dirt and spiders. So for the first three years we lived in our motor home while we demolished most of the interior. We moved walls, tore up the floor, jacked up the ceiling to make room for the small porch to be part of the kitchen. When we tore off the fireplace mica slate facing, we found dry rot had migrated all the way to the third floor. The heat vents had been covered up!

New plumbing, electrical service, radiant coils in the floor via the propane boiler, were on the agenda as well as a new roof and exterior paint. New garage doors replaced those falling off. Asphalt now covers the previously graveled driveway that washed out every year with the winter rains.

The workshop was built first so there would be a place for saws, drill press, grinder, planer, and the other instruments of construction. Husband did the fine carpentry work.

As well as the house, we had a lot of landscaping to address. Flower gardens on terraces, an orchard and vegetable garden where only weeds existed before. All this replaces blackberry vines and debris left by the second owner. The strange things we found under the house and in the swamp included a rubber boat, a metal boat, and hospital equipment.

The day after we moved up to these woods, during a record-breaking flood of the lowlands, disaster struck. Husband's father died, obliging him to fly to Arizona to bring his mother back to Washington. Not long after that, I fell through the floor we were removing in order to install a vapor barrier. I was lucky, no broken bones, but the skin and flesh were gone. Ick.

No sooner had I recovered from that accident, I sprained my ankle, slipping off a curb to a new patio we had put in. Life seemed to be getting back to normal when I dropped a pie dish and sliced my hand badly on the glass. I was starting to wonder what was making all these injuries happen.

Next came a silly slip of the ladle while I was cooking jam and I burned my hand. One day while sweeping debris from the driveway, I became short of breath. A trip to the emergency room revealed a pacemaker was needed. The following year another surgery removed a cyst from my spine that had affected the sciatic nerve. Ouch. The year after that was more surgery for a Morton's Neuroma, followed by Blepharoplasty.

By this time, I had started blaming the house for all my misery and misfortunes. Perhaps this millstone around my neck was responsible for my mishaps. Maybe it was jinxed; maybe it was my advanced age. Once the evil house idea was fixed in my brain, it was hard to shake. A day didn't go by that I wondered what would happen next, sure that I would croak before this darn place were finished. I saw no poltergeists, nor did I hear whispering in the walls, but I was becoming paranoid just the same. Each morning upon arising, a single thought ran through my brain: *what is going to happen today?*

Over the years, as we continued to labor daily around the property, I was reminded of my mortality. A badly twisted knee prompted the use of a thigh to ankle cast for six weeks. At least I was permitted to recover from one injury before another plagued me. I listed them as sprained ankle number two, a fall that took a great deal of skin off my arm. Then I came down with a debilitating bout of food poisoning. I won't go to *that* restaurant again.

There must have been something about this place. The ground? The water? The air? The house? One or more of these had caused all my accidents. Look at what happened to the two previous owners. Maybe the old beast just didn't want to be lived in. Was it sending me a message?

In spite of all this, I find now, after all the years dwelling here, it isn't that bad. The peace and tranquility of the area are so soothing that I no longer miss my old friends and family who occasionally come to visit. We have made new friends and enjoy a myriad of activities.

Sitting at the kitchen table today, looking out over the stream and the forest takes away the pain of everything that had been thrown at me. It is a joy to see Husband thriving, doing the things he had been longing for. He is engrossed in the hands-on building of the parts of the remodel that he can—slowly but surely.

After all we have endured, Husband assures me that my "accidents" were probably just carelessness and besides... I'm not sixty anymore.

Principally Amazing

By

Wilma F. Smith

I discovered that serving as principal of a first through eighth grade school in the country was not at all similar to being a principal of an elementary school in the suburbs. For one thing, I was pretty much on my own when it came to supervising teachers, disciplining students, or making sure the grounds were well kept. In the Edmonds School District, I had worked with two other women principals, although they were in their late fifties and I was a youngster of twenty-seven. But in Burlington I was a novelty (or oddity), since I was the only woman administrator in the district. Early in August 1970, a book salesman came by to push his company's new math series. When my secretary introduced him to me, his first words were, "What does it feel like to be a WOMAN principal?"

"Since I don't know how it feels to be a MAN principal, I can't really tell you what might be different for me," I said. "Let's just get down to business here, and you tell me why I should consider your math series."

Good grief. Here I was, in 1974, with two years' experience as a principal and a year as a special education administrator, and people still thought it strange that I should be competent enough to head up a school. My superintendent, Nat Moore, must have thought I was totally competent to handle almost anything.

Early one morning, a first grade teacher sent a student to the office to request my immediate assistance. When I arrived at her classroom, she introduced me to little Ellen, who, she said, had a story to tell me. Ellen would go with me to the office, she said. I took the little girl's hand and we walked down the hall together. I thought Ellen looked a bit upset, but she chattered about her new puppy, and took a little skip once in awhile.

I wished I had never had to hear Ellen's frightful story, but she proceeded bravely to recount the events of that morning.

"I got off the bus and a big boy came up to me. He said to come to the gym with him so he could show me something pretty."

"Did you go with him, Ellen?"

"Yes, Mrs. Smith, I did. He said to come up on the stage. There was a big mat on the floor. All at once, he pushed me down. He pulled off my panties, Mrs. Smith!"

She began to sob. "He was so mean! He lay down on top of me but I hit him in the face and he said 'OW' and jumped off. I got up quick and ran to tell Miss Lightbody."

"Oh, my dear," I said, hugging her. "You were so brave, and you did the right thing. Do you know this boy?"

"No ... but I can show you who he is if I see him."

I put Ellen in charge of the secretary, who gave her an ice cream bar and read her a story. I talked to both eighth grade teachers and we came up with a plan. I would set up a watch in the special education room where there was an observation booth with a one-way window. The teachers would send their boys through the room and I would sit in the booth with Ellen to see if she could identify the boy who had molested her.

Everyone stayed calm. The special education teacher took his students to the library while the teachers and I carried out our plan. Ellen rose to the occasion, scrutinizing each boy as he passed by the front of the room. Near the end of the line, she grabbed my arm.

"That's him! That's the boy who was mean to me."

She had identified a student who lived in a group home for juvenile offenders and was attending our school with special permission.

I hugged Ellen, and thanked the teachers for their help. My next unwelcome task was calling Ellen's parents. Thank God, they were not hysterical. In fact, they were calmer than I had been. I told them I would take Ellen and meet them at their doctor's office for an examination, and the district would pay for the office call. We carried out this plan, and the doctor found no harm had been done to this sweet little girl.

When I called the superintendent to tell him the details of the incident, he reacted dramatically.

"Well, you should have teachers posted every morning at all the doorways in the school! Maybe we should have a lockdown to be sure this boy hasn't run off. No, the district will not pay for any doctor's exam."

I assured him that teachers had regularly assigned hall supervision before school and that this was a strange happening that would not occur again. Further, I would pay for the doctor's office call myself.

This was the first time I had experienced the lack of support or understanding from my supervisor. But it would not be the last.

Sometime during the spring months of my first year as principal, a mother of an eighth grade girl came storming into the teacher's classroom and accosted the teacher.

"You can't make my daughter do this stupid homework!" she shouted, grabbing the teacher's arm.

Mrs. Ellington, a fiery redhead, firmly grasped the woman's other arm and walked her out of the classroom.

Shouts and disparaging remarks echoed down the hallway. I heard the commotion and met them outside my office door. Taking a quick look at Mrs. Ellington's red face, I spoke firmly to the mother, ushering her into my office. She would have none of civilized talk. "I want that teacher disciplined!" she shouted. "I'm coming back in an hour to beat her up and you can't stop me!"

As she raced out the door of the school, I called the superintendent. "I'll be over right away to discuss this," he said. Sure enough, minutes later, he appeared at my office door. Puffing on his pipe, he paced, agitated. I asked him to help me get a restraining order. He said he would need time to think about the implications of such an action. Then he looked out the window and saw the mother striding resolutely toward the front door.

"We'll talk about this later," he flung over his shoulder, as he quickly raced out of my office and out of the school the back way, through the kitchen entrance, leaving me to confront this angry woman unassisted. I offered her a chair, spoke to her in a quiet voice, and listened to her concerns. She gradually calmed down and agreed to talk to the teacher if I would sit in on the conference. That afternoon when school was dismissed, I met with Mrs. Ellington and the mother, listening to her concerns. By the end of our half-hour conference we had agreed on a course of action, and we parted company peacefully.

Some days it doesn't pay to get out of bed, I thought. All I ever wanted was to teach first grade!

As I sat at my desk early one morning, Kurt, a blue-eyed blonde eighth grader about four and a half feet tall, stood in the door, a downcast look on his face.

"Come in, Kurt!" I greeted him. "What's bothering our student body president this morning?"

"Oh, Mrs. Smith, my teacher sent me here to get a swat." Looking down at the floor, he continued. "I wadded up a paper and tossed it at Marvin. Right away Mr. Hagen grabbed my arm and shoved me out the door. He's really mad, I guess. Rats! I didn't mean to break the rule."

"Kurt, I hate to give you that swat, but I am going to get it over with as quickly as I can."

I got the worn wooden paddle out of the closet and showed it to him.

"As of today, you and I are going to make history at this school. I have never believed that hitting students was the best way to discipline them. So bend over and grab your ankles, and you'll have the honor of being the last student ever to get a swat from me."

"Okay, Mrs. Smith." He bent over, grabbed his ankles and shut his eyes tight.

I took a deep sigh and whacked him a good one on his butt. Smack! It was over. I gave him a hug and sent him back to his classroom, a sadder and wiser student body president. That incident firmed my resolve to outlaw corporal punishment in our school. Most of the teachers were relieved with my decision, and we worked together to develop alternate methods of disciplining our students.

Two days later, Douglas, another eighth grader, was ushered into my office by his teacher. I didn't like the smirk on his face as he squared his shoulders and looked at me defiantly.

Mr. Davis, his teacher, looked sternly at Douglas. "Tell Mrs. Smith what you have done."

"I didn't do anything," he said smugly. "Somebody stole a microscope from our science room and Mr. Davis says I did it. He has no proof!"

"Well, Douglas, let's take a look at your locker just to make sure. Come on."

The three of us walked down the hall, Douglas' feet dragging as he scuffed along. Yes, there in his locker, right under his gym clothes, sat the missing microscope. I took his arm firmly as he tried to escape.

"I am disappointed in you," I told him. "Before I decide what your discipline will be, I want to talk with your parents. So come back to my office and I'll call them."

Douglas sat slumped over in the office chair while I phoned his mother. She was not pleased. "I'll be over there right away," she said. "There has to be a mistake. My son would never steal anything."

Indeed, both of Douglas' parents refused to believe that he had taken the microscope. They continued to place the blame on someone else—anyone but their son. I told them I was sorry they could not see why I was suspending him from school for three days, but there it was. The three of them stomped out the door, muttering about my unfair actions.

Right, I thought. First grade would never have been like this.

The capper came along in the spring, when the students were outside for recess. As I hurriedly stuffed down my half sandwich in the teachers' lunchroom, a playground aide came in to fetch me.

"Come out in the hall, please, and talk to this young man. He's a fifth grader, but he came over to the primary kids' playground where the little girls were playing on the merry-go-round."

She took a deep breath as I faced Richard, who stood defiantly against the wall, his hands clenched at his sides.

The aide continued, "Richard was yanking up the skirts of the little girls! And he wouldn't stop when they cried. He was yanking and laughing and jumping up and down!"

"Richard, were you doing this?" I looked him in the eye.

"I was NOT! I was just running beside the merry-go-round and laughing. The girls got mad and told the duty."

"Now, Richard, if I asked those girls what happened, what would they say?"

He wouldn't answer, just stood there glaring at his shoes. I took him to the office and called his mother. She was there in ten minutes, huffing and puffing as she came in my door.

"What is this about my Richard?" She stood full height, hands on her hips, and glared at me.

"Please have a seat," I said. She plopped down in the rocking chair I kept in my office to calm down my visitors. I related the entire story to her, interrupted several times by Richard saying, "I didn't do it! I did NOT do it!" I insisted that numerous witnesses had reported Richard's behavior, but his mother would have none of it. She stood up, grabbed Richard's hand, and stared at me with a zombie-like expression.

"I don't believe you, Mrs. Smith. My Richard would never do such a thing. We are a Christian family, and he is a good soldier of the cross. It must have been this school atmosphere that would cause so many girls to lie about him."

I looked at her, my mouth open with surprise. But I was not prepared even yet for her final pronouncement. She stared, her eyes open wide.

"Oh, I see the anti-Christ!" she shrieked, pointing directly at me. I jerked my head around, looking behind me.

"Where?" I shouted. "I don't see him anywhere!"

With that, she grabbed Richard's arm and dragged him out of the office.

I gave a deep sigh and put my head down on my desk.

"And all I ever wanted was to teach first grade."

Wilma Smith

Writing Journeys with Wilma

When my elderly mother Esther arrived at my house with a large cardboard box full of letters and documents, I was motivated to write her life story. In this blog, I will highlight some of the steps I took to research, write, and refine the major events of her beautiful life.

Listening for Home

By

Sarah J. Stoner

I find it in the startled crow of the rooster.

The rooster—his feet in the moss, in the forest of the Great Northwest where I live right now, where I too stand right now.

And in his crow, his crow contains all that I was. That hollow space of sound contains all that I was. Memory rises up from my body as an ache from deep center, upwards, through my torso and up towards the leaning cedars.

Here I am, today, twenty-five years into life in America. A husband, two children, a house in the sweet-scented evergreen forests of northwest America.

And it's a damned chicken that startles me out of this place and back to Bangkok. Yes, a rooster's crow transports me to one of the largest cities on the globe. It might make sense if you, too, are a Third Culture Kid—maybe you, too, are a child born to North American parents, also who spent an entire childhood growing up beyond the boundary of America. Knowing nothing else, like all children who accept their lives as perfectly normal.

I moved from Belgium to Bangkok the same week I moved from twelve to thirteen. The stumbling chaos of Bangkok's streets—cars and vendor carts and motor scooters and the random rooster strutting through the rubble of a crumbled sidewalk—imprinted as home.

The old sounds own me. They startle me. I thought I *was* home. The coo of the morning dove, the sound of crickets at dawn and dusk, contain countries to which I once belonged. And as a white girl of German-Irish descent—I claim my ownership only within the spacious truth of my body. I wish for easy words to claim them out loud.

Inside, my body is a carved out emptiness. Inside, the phantom limb of childhood-now-gone plus country-now-unclaimable that only a girl gifted with multiple cultural foundations can know. That emptiness is the sound of a rooster's crow.

The pull of childhood-tightly-tied to country creates the Third Culture Kid in me. The layers sit inseparable within, and difficult to define. I hesitate to describe this type of memory out loud. I am afraid I will hear a story about someone's travels abroad as a response. Here, a strange uncomfortable defensiveness—protectiveness—rears up. *No. You do not understand. It is not the same. You cannot claim to know. My experience is not yours.*

Imagine telling a woman missing two legs that you once spent a month in a wheelchair. I believe your best intentions to connect to my experience. And I walk away alone—disconnected, mostly from myself.

I have only just begun to claim my inner spaces out loud. I am the body of many countries, molten countries in the porous core of a Third Culture Kid. I am TCK. No apologies if my origins are not tidy and definable. Maybe like sound or smell, it doesn't need explanation—only listening, inhaling deeply. Maybe I don't need words.

What if I claimed my space simply by fully filling it? Fulfill.

That rooster's crow reaches down to my bedrock and yanks something loose into my present. A lost piece of me wants to rise up, no, simply does rise up—quick like a balloon, only much larger. The piece contains everything, lifts me slightly from the country in which now I stand.

That hollow crow is like a mini near-death experience—or so I imagine. A moment that transcends time and words and even emotion—a moment that holds out my entire life for me to see again.

Does a TCK die like this every day?

I like living in the present. Fresh forest air glides over my skin, along with the sound of the creek that rushes over rocks and never stops for the slow gurgle of summer. Birds slide through the air, rest to weave a song and cast their net of melody into the trees. Worms and slugs and moss do their quiet heavy work. I want to be here.

But I am in Thailand, too. The young girl in rubber boots wading through the flooded streets to school that first August as a new eighth grader from Belgium, but not from Belgium because I was American, but not from America because I'd only visited America, never had lived there. It's a balloon of the confusion and lightness and freedom of not belonging.

My pipeline to that person finds its way to me through smell and sound. If these memories had a taste, they'd be sweet, pungent, and with just enough tang to make me sit up—and remember—who I am.

Sarah Stoner

Sarah Stoner is a fourth generation Washingtonian raised in Uganda, Morocco, Belgium, and Thailand. She lived in the U.S. for the first time at age 18. Her writing often explores nature, identity, and belonging.
sarahjstoner@hotmail.com

Short Works

By

Rita Sutker-Yucas

Sarah, the Soup Lady

My early years in Brooklyn afforded me the opportunity to observe many fascinating characters. None intrigued me more, however, than Sarah, the Soup Lady. At Goldfarb's deli, we counted the days of the week by her soup choices.

It was not until years later that I learned why Sarah never chose Goldfarb's specialty – the legendary chicken noodle.

She couldn't bring herself to eat it because her mother was serving that soup the night the Nazis took her away. So tonight, out of respect for Sarah, we will dine on tomato bisque and pray for peace in our world.

This Day

This day – so incredible that there can be no other
This day – so indisputable that thoughts cannot harm
This day – God's gift to our humanity – let us roll it around – savor it – digest its potential and build its body with love and respect.

1945

An excerpt from my novel

SWEPT BY THE TIDE

By

Joseph A. Vitovec

There was something peculiar about the sheets of rain flung at the windowpanes like a series of drumrolls driven by violent gusts of wind. Jolted, Jan looked up from his book.

Hunched over a garment she was stitching, Mother shifted her gaze to the window and froze. "What was that?"

Father cocked his head and listened for a few seconds. "Aw, just the rain." He dismissed her with a wave of his hand and turned back to his work.

"No, listen. I'm sure I heard something," she insisted.

The window rattled again in a succession of distinct, progressively louder raps. Someone was banging.

She turned ashen. "I told you I heard something! JesusMary, what's that? At this hour. Who could it be?" She let go of the garment and it slid to the floor.

The pounding became louder, insistent.

Eyes bulging with terror, she let out a gasp and crossed herself. "JesusMary, the Gestapo! They're the only ones who—Oh, my God! They're coming for us. They're coming for you!" She glared accusingly at Father. "You see what you've done? You and your cohorts!? You see? You see! Kubek must've talked. How many times did I tell you this would happen! Sooner or later. How many times—"

Father dove for the switch, snuffed out the light, and cautiously cracked open the blackout curtain.

Except for the sound of the rain, Mother's soft sobs, the crackling of the fire, and the measured ticking of the clock, the room was still, the tension palpable.

"That's not the Gestapo," he finally stammered with a sigh of relief. "They always come in twos. There's only one out there." He pulled shut the curtain and turned on the light. "Can't make out who it is." He grabbed a flashlight and scurried out of the room.

Straining to hear, Jan could just make out a hushed exchange, followed by heavy shuffling footsteps in the hallway, and then a knock. The door to the workroom flung open. Mother gave out a muffled cry. Jan gasped.

Framed by the doorway was a figure—a grotesque, demonic, rendering of a German soldier. Wearing a soaked filthy green uniform of the Wehrmacht, shredded in places, covered by dark oily stains, he was faceless—literally: a pair of whitish bony protrusions stuck out where his nose would have been; a mass of lumpy scar tissue congealed where his cheeks and lips had once formed a face. A pair of bulging, unblinking eyes peered from hollow, browless sockets. Only a few patches of stringy, matted hair covered a reddish, blotchy head when he doffed his sweat and grime-encrusted hat. Jan shivered. *The SS skull without the bones* flashed through his mind.

On his back, the stranger carried a lumpy rucksack. In his hand, a beat-up Mauser. *"Grüss Gott,"* he addressed Mother in German and then, correcting himself, "Good Evening," in a thickly accented Czech. *"Ich bin Ludwig."*

His inquiring look was met with blank stares.

"I'm Ludwig. Ludwig! Don't you remember me? Ludwig!"

Mother's jaw dropped as she eyed him incredulously. "Ludwig?" She took a hesitant step toward him and half-extended her hand. "Ludwig. Ludwig? You mean…" Her face came alive in a flash of understanding. "Oh my God! Ludwig! Ludwig Schreckinger! JesusMary." Her hand flew to her mouth. "JesusMary! I'm sorry! How could I—"

"Your mother, my mother…they're sisters." He grimaced, trying to smile. "Once, we came to see you. *Viele Jahre*… long ago."

"Yes, yes, I remember, of course!" she cried. "But Good God, what happened to you? You have to forgive me, I didn't recognize you. Oh my God." Tears welled up in her eyes. "What happened? How did you… I didn't know you were in the army. JesusMary! Come, come and sit down. You poor man. Come, come. Please."

He sighed. "A flame-thrower. At Stalingrad. Should've killed me, but somehow they managed to save me. Couldn't do much for me, though. No hospitals, no doctors."

"At least you're alive. That's what matters. But you, a soldier?"

"*Ja.* Got drafted. Like all the others. The right age, good health. You know. Had no choice. Everybody had to. Now they're grabbing even fifteen-year-olds and old men." He gave out a short, uneasy laugh, and winced as he shifted his rucksack. Grimacing, he slowly eased himself down into a chair. Father offered him a cigarette, which he snatched eagerly and lit with a shaking hand. He took a few deep drags, exhaling noisily. "And my aunt? How is she?" Squinting, he scanned the room. "Mother talked about her often. Misses her, you know. Said if I ever could, to stop and give her… give you our greetings."

"She died." Mother's eyes misted. "Over a year ago. Buried the day before All Souls Day."

Ludwig crossed himself. "May God rest her soul."

"Caught pneumonia."

He nodded and fell silent.

"Here, let me have your coat." Father helped him take off the rucksack. "And take off those wet clothes. We'll hang them by the stove. They'll be dry by morning." He raised his eyebrows at Jan, who reluctantly rose to assist.

"So that's your boy, eh?" Ludwig watched Jan wrestle the heavy rucksack off to the side. "It's Johann, isn't it? He's grown. How old is he now?"

"Almost fifteen," Mother said.

"You don't remember me," he turned to Jan, "but I saw you once when you were a little tyke. This big." His hand came down past his belt buckle. "That was the last time we came for a visit. Must've been '32 or '33. Long ago." He gave Jan a toothy smile.

Mother hung his overcoat over the back of a chair and pushed it near the stove. "Please, take off those clothes and put these on while I boil some water so you can clean up." She handed him a pair of Father's long johns and an old robe.

Jan took the uniform and hung it on the backs of a pair of chairs. It gave off a nauseating smorgasbord of putrid smells. Picking up Ludwig's boots, he noticed the hobnails gone from the soles and two gaping holes in their place.

They made small talk punctured by uneasy silences, until the hissing of boiling water spilling on top of the red-hot stove relieved them of their discomfort.

Mother and Jan carried the pot to the washroom and emptied it into the large wooden tub that took up most of the room. "The boy will help scrub your back, if you want. In the meantime, I'll heat up some soup. You must be starving." She waved off his profuse thanks and handed him a towel.

Ludwig undressed, exposing a mass of purplish scar tissue down to his waist. An ugly, brown knot stood out prominently against the pale flesh of his shoulder; another just below the shoulder blade, had turned deep purple. "Not pretty, eh?" He scowled.

Jan shrugged, trying to hide the sickening feeling in the pit of his stomach. He did not like to be left alone in the room with the German, even if he was a relation.

"Got these in Bosnia, back in '41. Still have a few pieces of shrapnel in my leg, too. Give me trouble each time the weather changes."

Jan sponged Ludwig's back, careful not to touch the scars, and flinched when he accidentally scratched the hardened knots of flesh. "Does it hurt when I touch it?"

"Naw, *nein*, it's fine now. You can press all you want." Ludwig let out a deep, contented sigh, as he sank deeper into the tub until his knobby knees rose to the stubble on his chin. "My first hot bath in months. In months! Would you believe it?" Eyes closed, he let out soft groans as Jan sponged his back. *"Das ist Himmel... das ist ein echte Himmel,* this is heaven," he murmured under his breath.

Ludwig was family, and therefore Jan should like him, or at least, respect him, feel sorry for him. But he was also a German. A Nazi! Recalling his last conversation with Grandmother before she died, he felt guilty for feeling resentment bordering on hatred toward this man, instead of compassion—not so much for what he was, but for what he represented. In his mind's eye, he saw other men, other Ludwigs, their faces blurred, save that of Fuchs as he pounded the Lederers—a vision that still haunted him. He saw Jakub's uncle in a heap in the dust. He saw Jakub's bloody face. He couldn't like this man. He dug his fingernails into the fleshy knots on the man's back.

Ludwig didn't flinch.

"Did you *kill* anybody in the war?" he blurted, barely able to contain his hostility. "Did you? Did you kill any Jews?"

Ludwig pulled himself up to an upright position, took the sponge from Jan's shaking hand, and eyed him thoughtfully for a few moments through the slits of his eyes. His contented smile vanished. "*Ja,* I killed people. I don't know if they were Jews or not."

Jan shifted uncomfortably.

"Let me tell you something, Johann," he said softly. "There's something you have to understand." His bulging, tired eyes searched Jan's face. "Look at me, boy. Look at me."

Jan met his look briefly but averted his eyes.

"War is a terrible thing," he went on. "Terrible! Don't ever forget it. No matter which side you're on. No matter what the reason. It's horrible. It makes you do things you never imagined you could. Back in '40, when I was drafted, it was, they said, to defend our *Vaterland*." It all seemed so clear then. So beautiful. Inspiring." The scars on his face twisted into a faint smile. "Anyway, that's what they told us we'd be doing. That's what everybody believed. I believed it. Everybody was raring to fight for the cause. And I tell you, I tell you, it felt great. It was almost... almost..." he searched for a word, "... almost spiritual." His eyes lost their dullness as his gaze shifted off into space. "The parades, girls throwing flowers at us, *ach Gott,* it was beautiful. Torches burning, bands playing, everybody singing *'Die Fahne Hoch.'* Believe me, Johann, it was so inspiring, you could cry. I cried! It didn't matter how you felt about the Party. Most people loved it, loved Hitler. Adored him. You couldn't help but feel the pride, real pride in being German. Being a patriot. Being part of history. Do you understand?" His unblinking eyes bore hard into Jan's face.

"I think so. My dad was a soldier, too. On the mountain."

Ludwig grunted gravely, gave him a smile, and slid down until only his head showed above the soapy water. He closed his eyes and, savoring the warmth, seemed to drift off.

"We used to go see him. He was going to fight for the Republic."

Peering at Jan through slits of eyes, Ludwig shook his head gravely. "You know, Johann, the idea, the idea of fighting for your fatherland is a great feeling, while it lasts. But the truth, the front, the fighting—*Scheisse*..." he swore "... that's different." He reached out, grabbed Jan's arm, and turned him until he faced him squarely. "You ask if I killed people, boy? Yeah, sure, I killed people. I did. You have to justify it to yourself, believe it. Maybe at first you think you're being a patriot, you're doing it for a cause, the right cause, of course, with God's help – *'Gott mit uns'* we used to say – but soon, you realize you have no choice. You do it to survive. It's really that simple. Black and white. You live or you die. And so you kill and go on doing it, not for the pretty girls and the parades, not even for something you believe. Patriotism is the furthest thing from your mind. You've long stopped believing it anyway. You do it to save yourself, to save your own skin. You kill, because if you don't kill the other poor bastard, who's just as scared as you are and for exactly the same reasons, the other poor bastard will kill you. It's that simple. Do you understand that, Johann? Can you understand?"

Jan eyed him with confused awe. Until now, it was easy to hate the Germans, all Germans, but this wretch of man was different, and not just because he was family. His anguish seemed genuine, his tone sincere. From somewhere within, Jan felt a creeping swell of compassion.

Ludwig stood up and wrapped himself in a towel. "My esteemed father, God bless him, his name was Ludwig, too, died in the bombing last year. He tried to warn me—about the war, I mean—but I wouldn't listen. I don't know if they told you, but he'd lost a leg at Arras. That was in the other war."

Jan shook his head.

"He was a great man, but I didn't take him seriously. What did he know? He was old." He sighed. "Anyway, I always wanted to be a teacher, write poetry, do good things. I believed in the word, the elegant word. Schiller, Goethe, Keats, Baudelaire. Loved 'em all. They were my heroes—my inspiration, my world. But then the war came and I was drafted. So, here I am—a cynic. *Dulce et Decorum Est,"* he said bitterly.

"I don't understand." Jan looked at him, bewildered.

"It's from a poem by Owen. Wilfred Owen—an Englishman. Forbidden by the *Reich,* of course, unfortunately. Someday you should read it if you can, and if the war turns out the way I think it will. Talks about how men are deceived into believing that it is 'sweet and proper,' those are his words, to die for one's country." A shadow washed over his face. "I've seen it, I've seen it all. There's nothing sweet about dying."

A steamy plate of warmed-over soup and a few slices of black bread lay waiting on the table as Jan and Ludwig returned to the kitchen. The wood in the stove crackled. The air hung heavy with the sour smell of the drying uniform. Gathered around the table, they all watched Ludwig make slurping sounds with each ladleful as he devoured the soup, and methodically wiped the empty dish with a piece of bread until it squeaked.

"We were retreating," he finally said, nodding thanks to Father for another cigarette, "making our way back from house to house, when they turned the flame-throwers on us. Killed a few, hurt many others. I got it full blast. What saved me, *Grüss Gott,"* he crossed himself, "I immediately buried my face in the snow. That probably saved my life. Passed out from the pain. Woke up in a field hospital, but all they could do for me was dress it. Sent me on to the rear, but they couldn't do anything, either. One night we got bombed, and the next thing I knew, everybody was gone. Everybody! Except us cripples, of course. That could only mean one thing—the Russkis! So I wasn't going to wait. Decided to go home."

"Oh, you poor, poor dear!" Mother cried out.

"You mean, you deserted?" Father peered at him sharply.

"In a way of speaking, perhaps." Ludwig took a deep breath and looked away. "Made my way back any way I could. Mostly on foot. At night. The Russkis shoot at anything that moves. Been on the road for weeks. Don't even know what I'm getting back to. Or if anyone's alive. Everything's in ruins. Haven't had news from home in months." A tear appeared in the corner of his eye and he wiped it with his fist. "Sometimes I feel ashamed to be a human being."

"And the war? How much longer do you think it's going to last?" Father leaned toward him in anticipation.

"Not much." He took a noisy drag and snuffed out the cigarette. "You see the convoys. You can see it on their faces. It's over."

He spent the night in what had been Grandmother's bed, tossing and turning, muttering something unintelligible between bouts of fitful snoring. He got up late and left after the noon meal. Mother stuffed his rucksack with fresh bread and a piece of moldy hard salami – the only meat she'd managed to squirrel away – and some of Father's underwear. After thanking profusely and embracing everyone, he hailed a ragtag convoy heading back toward Germany, gave a few waves from a truck that slowed down to let him jump aboard, and was gone.

"Boy, heard you talking to Ludwig while he was bathing. What did you talk about?" Father inquired when they found themselves alone.

Jan shrugged. “The war.”

“The war? He talked to you about the war?”

“He said wars are bad; said his father tried to talk him out of it.”

“Hmm. I remember the old fellow. Met him once or twice. Came home shell-shocked from the war. The First World War. They called it the war to end all wars, and look what happened.” He gave a short laugh. “It gave us the Republic. So, as far as wars go, there *are* some good wars – well, good isn’t the right word. Necessary maybe; yeah, that’s better. Necessary wars, like defending your country. Fighting for your country.”

“That’s what he said he was doing.”

“No, that’s not the same thing when you’re the invader. You remember the time on the mountain when we had to leave? When we had to leave without firing a shot? When we left without putting up a fight? Times like that, when you should’ve fought but didn’t, you lose your self-respect.” He swallowed hard and wiped his brow. “Something inside you dies. The more you think about what you should have done and didn’t, the worse you feel. You feel ashamed.” He looked at Jan through misty eyes. “There *are* times when living is worse than dying.”

JOSEPH A. VITOVEC

The Dark Side of the Cloth

By

Jean Wharton

"A moving column of carpenter ants would have felt more welcomed," I answer Deb's persistent, grim look now that the two of us are settled over our coffees. The top floor of the deli feels more like home than home, since Bligh crossed over, as he would say. "The days and hours no longer pop up in my head like numbers on a cash register machine. Progress of a sort," I say

"Give," she shoots at me. We'd known one another too long for her to mince words.

"I know, and yet I still don't believe it could happen," I mumble.

"You did check out that place beforehand, right?" Deb pushes on.

Jet lag doesn't slow Deb down, I silently note, and admit, "I went there once."

"And the dogcollars invited you back on that crucial day, Bligh and your anniversary—for wine and such. That's how they duped me into thinking I could leave you, hop off to London." Her louder, strident tone causes heads to turn, as she asserts, "I blame my stupidity for trusting a smelly dog—"

"Don't, Deb. Not today," I whisper, grabbing her arm—as if I could prevent her from spouting a stronger term than 'dogcollar' for clergy, or her usual 'stinky' for incense.

"Sorry, Pat." She plonks her larger hand on top of mine, squeezes, and takes it back. "You're certain you won't have a drop of.... Okay, tough it out." Well practiced, she unzips her jacket and smoothly reaches into a pocket, undoes the mini-flask, covering the Jack Daniels label with her other hand, pours several inches into her black coffee, screws the cap on and tucks the flask back. "My own distinctive brew," she informs the next table's open-mouthed, be-hatted dowager.

"Oh, my dear," she breathes. "I didn't intend to offend you in any way."

I jerk to life. *Ready, set,* I say to myself. Here *goes* Deb.

Deb scrunches her broad shoulders forward, turns full-faced that way and horse-whispers, "Pat here just lost her dreamboat."

Diamonds flash in an abrupt upswing to our neighbor's powdered jaw. "My poor Herbie passed...."

Don't, my head screams. *Oh, but she will.*

"Gas." Deb matter-of-factly adds. "Lots of corpses do that. Not Pat's hubby, mind you. Cremated. No chance to blow off contaminants."

An immobilized half-grimace on the dowager's reddening visage forces out of me, "As a new Santa Cruz UC graduate, Deborah worked in the mortuary industry." *This proper lady mustn't vomit here* I think, seeing her color fade, her lips compressing.

"Tea?" Deb asks, switching to her civilized mode. Elbows on our neighbor's table, Deb tentatively lifts the dowager's mini teapot, pours and sets it down. "I quite forgot," she says. "Cream in the cup first. Yes?" Cup and saucer in hand she heads behind the dowager to the counter.

"Friends become even more necessary at a time like this." The matron lowers her voice, leans in and asks, "She's not your sister, is she?"

"Only in a manner of speaking," I reply, dipping my gaze around the three white feathers that extend from her otherwise demure black cloche. I see what I dread, Deb succumbing to temptation. Deb's arm would have to fall off to prevent her doing what she's doing.

"You steeped it perfectly. Nice and dark," Deb congratulates the dowager. She centers the cup and saucer on the unfolded white hankie, and, like a diligent servant, Deb hovers asking, "More cream?"

God, what if Deb's about to tip an alcoholic off the wagon. "We distracted you. The tannic acid's too strong." I'm on my feet. "Why don't I run downstairs and fetch a new cup?" I lock eyes with Deb. She knows I know she's doctored the brew.

"What a sweet fuss you two are making over me," the dowager says in a brand new, mother-addressing-her-brood tone. "Do come and join me."

Deb actually does as told. We flank the matron.

Oozing calm, "Much nicer, girls. I'll begin the introductions. I'm Millicent Umborough, widow of the late Right Reverend Montagu Herbert Castillon Umborough, Bishop of the Diocese of—"

"God!" Deb moistens her lips as if relishing her next bite. "May I?" she enquires, and forthwith stirs Millicent's brew. And just as easily, she betrays me.

"Patagonia Rae Brown," she firmly states, indicating me.

"Pat," I mumble—too late.

The dowager smiles. "Never reduce your title." She clarifies, "You may address me as 'Miss Millicent' and I shall introduce you to all and sundry...." As if presenting a debutante at court, she rings out, "Miss Pa - ta - go - nia." One hand gesturing, she preaches at me, "Practice in your imagination, hold your head high." Palm up and elevating, "You are the Queen of Tonga." Fingers streak down. "Rain pouring buckets, you ride in an open carriage in Queen Elizabeth's coronation parade. She is the 'raining' monarch of all time, you know." Her fingers find my chin, "Up Pa - ta - go - nia. Demonstrate royalty, no matter your country." She raises her cup, toasts me and downs a large swallow.

Deb follows suit.

Millicent's soft brown eyes, so like my Mum's, draw me in. *Mum gone an aching fifteen years ago yesterday, little wonder,* I muse, *that Bligh's death, fifty-three days past, smarts too much to chat about him to a stranger. It'd be like reading someone else's obituary.*

"Pat, you haven't touched your coffee." Deb's words do it.

Tears. I jamb my fist into my cheek and excuse myself. By the time I return from the restroom the two have cozied together. Plot like, they eye me as I approach and slide onto my designated hot seat. *Oh,* goes my brain, at last in gear, *Deb's arranged this entire charade to buck me up. The woman's a hired actress. Did Deb forfeit her London visit to pay her and together rehearse their parts for my sake?* Deb's authentic disdain tunes me in.

"It's that bloo... blankety blank institution. Millie, you of all people have to know how god-awful it is to be left in the clutches of an established religion. Pat's deceased was a priest. Did you have to put up with daily mumbo-jumbo from Herbie? *And* bowing to the tri-clan's symbols?"

Millicent gasps, "You mean our Christian Three-in-One, Triune God?" Her watery eyes, her mouth corners fixed down, portray a genuine dejected expression.

Deb spiels on, "If that isn't bad enough, Pat and Blighty had a full blown religious salon-cum-chapel installed on the second floor of their house—gothic screens, wide table high altar, fancy linens. A great Hallowe'en backdrop, I told her, but she'd lost her sense of humor once she tied the knot with that literal urgy hokus-pokus."

Liturgy jams in my throat. Deb's familiar, pickled description of religious life, once sure to make me laugh, becomes part of the charade. *Get even,* my head demands, flashing a silly image of me staggering out of the now packed deli, each arm propping up a besotted female. Deb true to Deb, that Jack Daniels is no brown liquid stage prop. They're ticking up the blood alcohol points.

I let fly. "My friend here, Deborah Felicity Kovak, a devout agnostic, true to a neither God nor no God life, may send random acts of kindness your way. Or," I wince as Deb's kick strikes my shin. Defiant, I shift sideways toward her co-conspirator, and trek on. "Or Deb, D for despotic, may sling your way random acts of quite another ilk. Brilliant at bullseye on both."

As if I had said, *Deb has a toothache,* true to her bishop's wife's character, Millicent purrs at Deb, "I'll pray for you." Her tone firmer, she admonishes, "Remember, Felicity means faithful. Tell me, dear, your father clung to agnosticism, did he?"

Deb squirms convincingly. "A rabid atheist," she avows. And, needing no rehearsal, downs her drink to the mug's shiny bottom.

Seeing Millicent precisely duplicating Deb's chug-a-lug, I stifle a cheer. A clang of cutlery hitting tile pulls me out of their theater orbit. I leave them to retrieve a child's spoon off the floor. That done, I eye the thespians anew.

Deb springs up and makes off, Millicent's tea cup and her own coffee mug in hand.

Counting on mere seconds alone with the paid actress, I hurry to commend Millicent on her utterly believable performance and ask her her last role.

Eyebrows raised, she forces her upper lip down hard, causing her nose to elongate. "I never change roles, Patagonia," she affirms, and shifts her focus toward Deb.

The furthest Deb had gone before today comprised a genuine, fully decked out circus clown, with barrel organ and spider monkey for props. Deb snuck him into the parish hall, easily diverting children from the church Easter egg hunt. There they whooped, screamed, and strummed their freedom from adult control on the parish hall piano, unwittingly singing heathen songs scripted by Deb for the clown. The mites gobbled chocolate eggs and rabbits galore. Then bashed one another with empty baskets, until the Sunday School teacher unlocked the door. I stifle a giggle remembering how Miss Prim and Proper was rescued by the arms of the hired clown from the flood of children fleeing the paschal debris scene. Deb's excuse: clown and teacher—both shy before Deb's choreographed church debut—began courting that day.

"Did you improve the brew again, Deb?" I ask.

She bangs her mug on to the table, and glares at me.

"Your school chum divulged no local church secrets," the actress says, resuming her mothering voice.

"Drop the curtain on your charade this minute." I hear the anger in my voice, the first time since Bligh left.

Millicent's beginning retort, "Even a widow must..." weaves well with Deb's, "An accusation lacking merit," that stops short of the actress's, "... observe a certain decorum."

Now I'm steamed. "The two of you should go into the identity theft business together," I say. "Bishop and Kovak."

"Hey, Pat, bridle your tongue," Deb snaps back. "I've not met any purple's wife till today. You shouldn't insult one of your own."

"Bishop's," Millicent corrects Deb, adding quietly, "It's true bishops wear purple shirts." She taps my shoulder. Her tone contrite she murmurs, "I only wanted to comfort another clergy widow."

"Yes, of course you did, Millie," Deb seconds her.

Jesus! I hear in my head. *Millicent's for real. Deb's backing a bishop's wife—not an actress. Punt.* As if my brain's a roulette wheel, spinning only one marble idea per patron, I blurt, "The high count on identity thefts in this state make us all leery."

Deb jumps on it. "Three tries at identity swipes in seven years, Pat ... a - go - nia has had. Hers, not Blighty's. He handed his pitiful earnings over to Pat, the accountant here."

As if on cue, Millicent unsnaps her narrow long handbag and tips the contents on to the table. A passport. Two? Three?

My jubilant thought—*We've nabbed a major thief*—is flattened.

"Don't look so alarmed, my dears. Papa, the ambassador, was a stickler for every milligram of documentation any official might want to see," she explains. "He drummed into my head follow the rules for that country. Don't comply with petty officialdom. Plow them under. Hence he arranged what you see." Obscuring the cover of each one as she reveals its contents to us only, she whispers, "French for France," drops it into the handbag. "Canadian for Canada, and many domains." Gone. "Diplomatic for sticky places and an ordinary U.S. one because this is home. Oh, and one I may not reveal."

"Disguised are you?" Deb asks.

Busily stowing the passports, Millicent ignores Deb's question. Her gaze imperial, she crows at me, "Let us now praise ingenious women and hear your dilemma, Miss Patagonia."

I let out a long breath of exhaustion. "Bligh went peacefully asleep and never woke up. I found him about seven—"

"It took me ten minutes to get there," Deb interjects. "A sheriff and a couple of patrolmen had arrived already."

"Uniforms flooded my kitchen. A little woman called a grief counselor held my elbow and nudged me into the front room. She kept saying the same thing over and over that I'd be in a fog. I didn't have the heart to tell her that in any crisis I'm clear as a church steeple bell."

"And who came from your church?" Millicent prompts.

"A young woman priest and a black bishop. I'd heard his name. He's newly semi-retired and had moved to the next town. I can see his dimples now. He smiled slowly and his whole face lit up. Gorgeous dimples. He said he had them as a child, got skinny and lost them, and recently got them back. Funny that his every word seems chiseled into my brain. Then this silly woman priest interrupted us. *Where's Bligh?* she asked. And again when I pretended not to hear her. Where the deuce did she imagine? That he'd gone south instead of—"

"Did the female priest upset you?" Millicent persists.

"No. The stonewalling came weeks later."

"Pat, let me tell it, and you can chime in on the parts I get wrong. Deal?" We slap hands. Deb makes not one mistake, not even when she tells who came to take away Bligh's altar and prayer bench and throne. She even mentions that Bligh was nominated once to become a Bishop. "He didn't make it," Deb notes, adding, "I did not utter a prayer. Not me. I put in a petition to a fellow doubter, Thomas, the one who collected hard data. I wager that the other one called Saint Peter runs the admission, pearly white gates, while Thomas, a saner being like me, occupies the sentinel box and maneuvers the purple for bishop, signal crossing bar. *Up* to admit. *Down* to deny."

"Deb, bless you!" I get up, and go round Millicent to give Deb a hug. I had detested the idea of re-locating, re-starting my accountancy practice, unbolting the rood and side screens from the chapel floor—like taking apart the substance of our lives.

"Oh, Bligh's altar," I say. "They've buried it deep in the wrong place and gagged me with prayer cards, and 'Good and Faithful Servant' messages, as if I'll keep quiet while his ecclesiastical things scatter like mustard seed on sandy ground."

"I'll get to the bottom of this!" Millicent says, her mouth set in a line, and brings out a small purple notebook. "Come along, Herbie," she near cajoles. "The Lord is not quite done with us yet. He intends us to shed some light behind the dark folds of the cloth. Details, girls. First, the names of the miscreants."

"Amen to that," says Deb, quickly adding, "Don't quote me."

Sounding more like myself, I rejoice in mimicking her English ancestors. "I jolly well shall quote you, Deborah Faithful Kovak. Amen!!"

Jean Wharton

In her childhood English seaside home, Broadstairs, Dickens favorite watering place, Jean poured her abundant energy into dance, acrobatics, drama and school. At 19, the land of opportunity—America—calling, she joined the postwar brain drain, and emigrated. Sidetracked by marriage and travel, not until California did she find what she craved. One Ph.D. later, halfway through her first year of university teaching, a distracted driver T-boned her car. Complications forced change, somersaulting her toward the Pacific Northwest, an externship at Children's Hospital, Seattle, and a career in family therapy. Dickens might smile at this piece and at the book to follow.

SKAGIT VALLEY WRITERS LEAGUE, LOOKING BACK, LOOKING AHEAD

BY

HEMLATA (HEMA) VASAVADA

In 1958 six creative writing students from Skagit Valley College—Molly Dawdle, Marilyn Johnson, Florence Logsdon, Gladys McCune, Junia Palmer, and Pat Talbert—formed a group to share their work, provide each other with constructive critiques, and exchange information about markets. They met once a month at Marilyn Johnson's home. As word spread, other writers, including several men, joined the group, and they began meeting at the Mount Vernon Library.

I had the good fortune to be acquainted with three members who had joined the group in its infancy. Ken Fenske, a published author of children's stories, poems, and short stories, brought his experiences of working as a concert pianist/organist, music teacher, and music director for a Hollywood party boat, touring the LA Harbor with actors and singers, and turned them into stories. Florence Logsdon Anderson, was an original member whose articles were published in several magazines. Marjorie Russo, a newspaper columnist and World War II veteran, shared her writing skills with the members. The three have passed on, but the league continues with new members and new ideas.

As the League membership and leadership changed, the group adjusted accordingly. When I first joined in 1976, Marjorie Russo showed me how to revise and move sentences by cutting them out of the paper and taping them where they would fit better. Even after I acquired a computer, she brought over her scissors to cut and tape her story. Writers still cut and paste, although without scissors or Scotch Tape.

Through the years the members have held contests for school children to promote writing. Members have also attended conferences, conducted workshops, and invited authors to make presentations. To celebrate the 100th Anniversary of Skagit County in 1983, the League compiled a booklet: *Authors of Skagit County.* We published anthologies in 2000, 2005, and 2008; the last one was published to celebrate the 50th Anniversary of the Skagit Valley Writers League.

The League is still fulfilling the needs of its members as it has done in the past. Through general meetings and critique sub-groups of four or five each, the members help with editing, share in each other's successes, and comfort each other during the agonies of revisions and rejections.

The group has moved forward to meet the demands of present times by developing a website, organizing Writers Theatres, and arranging workshops on marketing, publishing, and improving the craft.

The six members who started the Skagit Valley Writers League in 1958 have grown to more than seventy in 2014. Looking back, we thank our founding members for our beginning, and thank those who came after them for their contributions in helping the League grow. Looking ahead, we will continue to provide a forum for the community of writers. With dedicated and skilled leaders and enthusiastic members, the League has entered the 21st century publishing world and continues to be a haven for writers.

Hemlata (Hema) Vasavada

Hemlata (Hema) Vasavada was born in Jodhpur, India, where she earned a master's in philosophy. She immigrated to the United States in 1968 with her husband and their (then) one-year-old daughter. She has conducted workshops through Literacy Volunteers of America to train volunteers in English as a Second Language teaching techniques, and held offices of president, vice-president and treasurer at Skagit Valley Writers League. Her articles and humor essays have been published in magazines and newspapers. Her novel, The Cascade Winners was recently published. She and her husband moved to Pullman, Washington to be near their daughter and family.